Methodology

A Pocket Guide to Reduce Cost and
Improve Value Through Function Analysis

James D. Bolton, PE, CVS, PVM
Whirlpool

Don J. Gerhardt, PhD, PE, CVS
Ingersoll-Rand

Michael P. Holt, PE, FSAVE, CVS
U.S. Army Corps of Engineers

Stephen J. Kirk, PhD, FAIA, FSAVE, CVS, LEED® AP
Kirk Associates, LLC

Bruce L. Lenzer, FSAVE, CVS, CQM/OE
Synergy Value Solutions, LLC

Mary Ann W. Lewis, FSAVE
Lewis & Zimmerman Associates

Donald E. Parker, PE, FSAVE, CVS
Consultant

James A. Rains Jr., FSAVE, CVS, PVM
Advanced Value Group, LLC

James R. Vickers
Raytheon

GOAL/QPC

Value Methodology

Development Team

Susan Griebel, *Project Leader*
Janet MacCausland, *Cover and Icon Design*
nSight, Inc., *Project Editing and Layout*

GOAL/QPC

12 Manor Parkway, Salem, NH 03079-2862

Toll free: 800-643-4316 **or** 603-893-1944
Fax: 603-870-9122
E-mail: service@goalqpc.com
Web site: www.MemoryJogger.com

Printed in the United States of America

First Edition
10 9 8 7 6 5 4 3 2

ISBN 978-1-57681-105-4

Acknowledgments

We offer our sincere thanks to the many friends and devoted value engineers who have contributed to the development of this pocket guide. We dedicate the work to those who have come before us, notably, Lawrence D. Miles and Eleanor Miles-Walker, Carlos Fallon, Eugene Smith, Fred Sherwin, and William Lenzer.

We also thank the Directors and Friends of the Lawrence D. Miles Value Foundation who provided support and guidance to the authors.

Rudy H. Kempter, FSAVE, CVS
MVF Director, The Kempter Group

Robert H. Mitchell, FSAVE, CVS
MVF Director

Axel Peter Ried, FSAVE, CVS
MVF Director, Ried Management Methods

David C. Wilson, P.Eng, CVS
*MVF Director, SAVE International
President, NCE Value Engineers, Inc.*

Theodore C. Fowler, FSAVE, CVS
Fowler & Whitestone

Jay Mandelbaum, PhD

John E. Sloggy, CVS
Value Based Design, LLC

Contents

Introduction ix

1 History of Value Methodology 1

2 Establishing a Value Program 3

Find Your Champion! 3

Your Organization's VM Policy – How
    to Develop One! 4

What is a VPS? 5

Why a VPS? 5

Objectives and Purposes of the VPS 5

What does a VPS contain? 5

3 Project Selection 9

How do I select projects for a value study? 9

Timing 13

Manufacturing 13

Management Applications 14

4 Conducting a VM Workshop 15

Workshop Site 15

Workshop Room Environment 16

Required Materials and Logistics 17

Facilitation Skills 18

**5 Team Member Selection and
   Team Building 20**

Selecting the VM Team 20

Team Building 23

6 The Value Methodology Job Plan 25

Application of the VM Job Plan 25

Preworkshop Activities 27

Facilitator Preparation 37

7 The Value Methodology Job Plan: Workshop Activities 38

Information Phase..38
Function Analysis Phase 39
Creative Phase..51
Evaluation Phase...53
Development Phase..61
Presentation Phase..66

8 The Value Methodology Job Plan: Postworkshop Activities....................73

Implementation Phase.....................................73
Follow-up Phase..74
Conclusion 75

9 Contractual Aspects of Value Engineering for the U.S. Government 76

Appendix A Function Analysis Systems Technique 95

Appendix B Delphi...101

Appendix C Target Costing 109

Appendix D Voice of the Customer and Quality Function Deployment 114

Appendix E Lean Enterprise Value....................120

Appendix F Design for Manufacture and Assembly 127

Appendix G Theory of Inventive Problem Solving 137

Appendix H   Tear-Down Analysis *148*

Appendix I   Weighted Evaluation Technique *153*

*Appendix J   Leadership in Energy and Environ-
mental Design (Sustainability) Checklist* *159*

Appendix K   Life Cycle Costing *161*

Appendix L   Choosing By Advantages *172*

Appendix M   Value Improving Practices *184*

*Appendix N   Introduction to the Value
Dictionary* *185*

Suggested Readings *194*

Index *195*

Introduction

What Is Value?

Value is defined as a fair return or the equivalent in goods, services, or money for something exchanged. It is represented by the relationship:

$$\text{Value} \approx \text{Function/Resources}$$

Function is measured by the performance requirements of the customer, and resources are measured in the materials, labor, price, time, etc., required to accomplish that function.

Value Methodology (VM) focuses on improving value by identifying the most resource-efficient way to reliably accomplish a function that meets the performance expectations of the customer.

What are Value Methodology, Value Analysis, and Value Engineering?

Value Methodology (VM) is a systematic process used by a multidisciplinary team to improve the value of a project through the analysis of its functions. The VM process comprises techniques that enable the project team to provide the highest value products, projects, processes, and services to the customer.

The term Value Analysis (VA) is typically used when applying the VM process to existing applications, such as manufactured goods. The term Value Engineering (VE) is used when applying VM to new products, construction projects, processes, and services. Facilities and construction projects include buildings, highways, airports, dams, refineries, wastewater treatment plants, and so on.

Key concepts include understanding the functions that the customer values and using function analysis to provide the functions and quality at the lowest total life cycle cost. A multidisciplinary team approach is used. Experts from the project's disciplines participate on the team. The team leader is certified in VM techniques.

The Society of American Value Engineers International (*www.value-eng.org*) is the professional society for VM. It maintains VM standards and body of knowledge, which may be accessed through the organization. The process for applying VM is referred to as the Value Methodology Job Plan, which consists of the following three stages:

- Preworkshop activities.
- VM workshop activities.
- Postworkshop activities.

The VM workshop activities consist of the following six phases, which are conducted sequentially:

1. **Information phase.**
2. **Function analysis phase.**
3. **Creative phase.**
4. **Evaluation phase.**
5. **Development phase.**
6. **Presentation phase.**

VM is a process to:

- Identify unnecessary cost in a project.
- Offer alternatives while assuring that quality, reliability, life cycle cost, and other critical factors meet or exceed the customer's expectations.

VM is not:

- Cost cutting.

- Quality reduction.
- A process that can be applied without top management support and the support of all functional disciplines.

All activity in VM focuses on providing the highest value to customers. Quality and functions are improved while spending less money and using fewer resources.

What makes VM unique?

VM is unique compared to other practices, such as Total Quality Management, Lean Manufacturing, and Six Sigma, because analyzing functions and providing the highest value to the customer in a formal, step-by-step process are the foundations of VM. Function analysis, the multidisciplinary team approach, and the formal job plan make VM like no other management practice.

How to use this book

This book offers you the history, methodology, and applications of the VM so you will be able to successfully apply the practice within your business. This information is useful to all stakeholders of any process, project, product, or service, whether you are the owner, the designer, the manufacturer, or the customer.

Analyzing functions, cost, and your criteria for success will enable you to objectively define the solution that will spell success! We hope that the VM Job Plan, the tools, the applications, and the examples you find in this pocket guide will enable you to expand your understanding of the VM and inspire you to new and creative uses of the practice in your own business!

Chapter 1

History of Value Methodology

Value Analysis (VA) was conceived in the 1940s by Lawrence D. Miles, an engineer who was employed in the Purchasing Department at General Electric. He focused on the functions of manufactured components and created the process of function analysis, which evolved into a formal practice called Value Analysis.

The benefits of VA became readily apparent and the technique was adopted by many organizations and government agencies during the 1950s. Many applications beyond product design were developed during the early growth of Value Methodology (VM).

The Society of American Value Engineers was incorporated in 1959. The name of the value society was changed to SAVE International in 1996 to reflect the worldwide growth of the field of Value Methodology. SAVE International sponsors an annual conference where technical papers on the latest VM techniques are presented. Approximately forty countries have very successful VM societies.

Many individuals and corporations have contributed greatly to the practice of VM by developing related techniques. These include:

- Function Analysis System Technique (FAST) Diagram, which was created by Charles Bytheway during the 1960s.

- Target Costing, which originated at Toyota in 1959.

- Quality Function Deployment (QFD), which was introduced by Yoji Akao in 1966.

- Zero and First Look Value Engineering (VE) in new product development.

- VA/VE Tear-down, which General Motors and others developed as a competitive analysis during the 1960s and Isuzu further refined during the 1970s.

- Theory of Inventive Problem Solving (TRIZ) Systematic Innovation Process, into which Genrich Altshuller incorporated principles of function analysis.

Design for Manufacture and Assembly (DFMA), which was developed by Geoffrey Boothroyd and Peter Dewhurst and has become a useful VM tool.

The Lawrence D. Miles Value Foundation (*www.value foundation.org*) is a nonprofit 501(c)(3) foundation that strives to develop, apply, and promote the use of VM worldwide. Its mission—to educate, innovate, and advocate—is evidenced by the Foundation's work in bringing the study of VM to college and university undergraduate and graduate programs in engineering, architecture, and business, as well as by its partnership with GOAL/QPC to create this pocket guide.

Chapter 2

Establishing a Value Program

Find Your Champion!

Every successful management practice has had a champion at the highest level of the company or organization. General Electric supported Larry Miles in the development and implementation of VA in the 1940s. As secretary of defense in the 1960s, Robert McNamara was committed to VM and inspired the Department of Defense to adopt the practice. Bob Galvin, CEO of Motorola, took quality seriously in order to survive in the marketplace. He championed the Six Sigma process and turned Motorola into a company renowned for quality and profitability. General Electric again took a lead in applying best practices when Jack Welch followed suit and also championed the application of Six Sigma, making it a household name. Since the 1990s, every major corporation in the process industry, whether petrochemical or pharmaceutical, and including technology-based and science-based innovation companies such as DuPont, Ingersoll-Rand, and Raytheon, has had leaders at the very top who champion value-improving practices.

VM enables the organization to retain its competitive advantage, increase profitability, and generate visible improvement to the bottom line. VM is a mature practice that your organization needs in order to achieve success in today's global business environment.

For a Value Program to excel, an organization also needs a champion. It is the first step to success. There are a few ways to approach the task of identifying and gaining commitment at the top so that VM becomes part of the organization's culture for continuous improvement.

1. **Within your own business practice, identify the person who has a need and is willing to apply VM to a specific project, product, or process.** That need may be driven by such motivations as the desire to reduce cost, to increase profitability, or to create innovation. Find that project manager who is creative and proactive and has a need! This approach starts in the ranks. Success stories then flow upward in the organization, and a champion may be found at a high level based on the commitment within the mid-level and the results of the applications.

2. **Alternatively, go to the top! Find the opportunities to present the concept of creating a Value Program within your organization.** Build the business case to demonstrate the need, the applications, the potential return on investment, and the related successes among your competitors. Then strategize on the best way to catch the eye of those at the top. Speak at conferences where they will be present, meet face-to-face with the person(s) you have identified as the potential champion(s) and make your case, and use contacts you have near the top to make your case first so they can open the next door for you!

The luck of finding your champion is a matter of preparation meeting opportunity, as the Roman Philosopher Seneca would say. So, be prepared and take that opportunity!

Your Organization's VM Policy – How to Develop One!

No organizational unit, least of all a VM group, can operate in a vacuum. VM needs visible management support as evidenced by a strong comprehensive policy statement from top management in organizations of every size.

The top level of VM is a staff function, not a line function. It is weaker than a line function in that it deals with people over whom it has no direct authority.

What is a VPS?

The Value Policy Statement (VPS) is a visible record of VM acceptance by your organization's senior management. It signifies acceptance, endorsement, and encouragement and defines the relationships with other departments.

Why a VPS?

A VPS is necessary to clearly demonstrate management support and commitment.

Objectives and Purposes of the VPS

The objectives and purposes of the VPS are the following:

- To create the staff function.
- To provide assistance in relating to other line elements.
- To establish an annual budget.
- To show strong organizational leadership.
- To define accountability.
- To sustain a positive effort.

What does a VPS contain?

A VPS contains the following:

- A statement permitting professional review of the organization's products, processes, and services.
- Guidelines for establishing Value Programs in each division.

- Annual goals for:
  - The application of VM, e.g., VE will be performed on every project with a dollar value greater than $x; VE will be performed on the projects, products, or processes which represent 80% of the organization's annual budget (Pareto's Law demonstrates that this will be approximately 20% of the organization's projects, products, or processes).
  - Implementation, e.g., to achieve a percentage of the organization's total annual budget as implemented savings.

Suggested VM performance indicators are shown in the following table.

Value Methodology Performance Indicators

Performance Indicator	Internal Program		External Program	
	Current Year	Next Year	Current Year	Next Year
Amount Budgeted				
Number of Employees Trained				
Number of Contract Proposals				
Number of Internal Studies				

Continued on next page

Continued on next page

Value Methodology Performance Indicators
(continued)

Performance Indicator	Internal Program		External Program	
	Current Year	Next Year	Current Year	Next Year
Percentage Approved				
Average Approval Time				
Rate of Return on Investment				
Percentage of Business Affected				
Percentage of Savings Achieved				

The VPS also describes the essential elements of a Value Program:

- Job positions with functional responsibilities.
- Selection and appointment of qualified personnel.
- Broad educational programs in value techniques.
- Standard procedures.
- Controls to minimize unnecessary product costs.
- Definitions, as required.

The goals and objectives of the VM staff are:

- To train the organization.
- To motivate their colleagues.
- To champion the use of VM within the organization.
- To develop new techniques that meet company goals and objectives.
- To prepare Value Change Proposals (VCP) in workshops.

The VM staff have generally two categories of responsibilities:

1. **Those specific to VM:**
   - Identify functions within the organization's projects, products, and processes in order to identify opportunities to apply VM within the organization.
   - Apply the VM Job Plan structured methodology by facilitating value workshops.
   - Assist the decisionmakers in implementing VCPs.

2. **Those to advance the art:**
   - Broaden the use of the VM.
   - Extend benefits to other parts of the organization.

Chapter 3

Project Selection

How do I select projects for a value study?

Several factors help the decisionmaker to determine whether a product, project, process, or service is a candidate for a value study. Consider candidates based on applying VM to:

1. Products or projects methodically, at predetermined stages in their development.

2. Programs according to Pareto's Law of Distribution.

3. Products or projects over budget.

4. Products or projects with conflict.

5. Products or projects based on viability.

6. Complex products or projects.

7. Prototypes.

Let's examine each of these factors in more detail. Consider:

1. **Applying VM to products or projects methodically at predetermined stages in their development.** Management may wish to set a policy for the application of VM on any product or project within the organization. Early application of VM in the design

process is the most effective since a change in the design or a redirection of the program can easily be made in the early stages and will save the owner and user time and money in the long run. The following figure depicts the decisionmaker's influence on life cycle costs in a typical public construction project. The early application of VM will have the greatest effect on life cycle costs.

Decisionmaker's Influence on Life Cycle Costs of a Typical Building

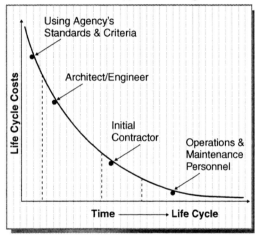

2. **Applying VM to programs according to Pareto's Law of Distribution.** Analyze the costs of your program to understand where the high costs exist. Typically, 80% of the program costs may be found in 20% of the projects or items that comprise the program. For example, in a municipality's capital improvement program, which is made up of multiple projects that

must be accomplished over a period of time, you may find that 20% of those projects represent the greatest dollar value, or roughly 80% of the value according to Pareto's Law of Distribution. Those projects are clear candidates for VM.

A manufacturer may have a product line of many products, such as cell phones, engines, and missiles. The decisionmaker may analyze the product line using Pareto's Law of Distribution to determine which products are the greatest revenue generators —again, 80% of the revenue may be generated by 20% of the products. It may be useful to apply VM to those products since the results of the VM effort may reduce time to market, improve quality, improve technology, decrease initial and life cycle costs, and increase profits.

3. **Applying VM to products or projects over budget.** All products and projects routinely face budget challenges. VM may be applied when a product or project is over budget. The team may focus on ways to avoid cost overruns.

4. **Applying VM to products or projects with conflict.** The development of products and projects involves many stakeholders, including the owners, project managers, designers, users, operators, regulatory agencies, and others. The natural process of conceiving and designing a product or a project involves conflict, and in some cases, that conflict escalates due to competing priorities. VM may be applied as an objective second look at any stage of design or production. The value process enables a team to clearly define needs versus wants and to prioritize those items.

5. **Applying VM to products or projects based on viability.** Viability is the crux of the matter. Can a cell phone be designed with all of the desired

amenities (e-mail, camera, web access, size, style), manufactured, and marketed on time and at a price the customer is willing to pay? Can the elementary school be designed to accommodate the students, the teachers, security, and accessibility while meeting all government regulations and the budget? When a project manager questions the viability of the product or project—when his/her gut says that he/she can't get to market on time or on budget with the best product or project—then VM is one way to objectively analyze the effort to assess the technical and nontechnical components and cost elements to determine if redirection is necessary.

6. **Applying VM to complex products or projects.** Use VM to ensure that all of the basic functions have been well defined and are being met by the design; to identify and offer alternatives to high-cost elements to ensure that best value and best life-cycle cost applications have been considered; and to analyze the project from a multidisciplinary perspective to ensure that the disciplines and costs have been well conceived and interconnect well.

7. **Applying VM to prototypes.** Use VM on products or projects that will be replicated. The savings and improvements identified in the first application may be applied across the board to all other uses. For example, improvements (whether technical or cost) to the design of a widget may be replicated millions of times. The technical changes to a standard military barracks design may be replicated at army bases across the United States.

Owners and project managers use VM for many and varied reasons. Determine the best uses in your practice, apply VM, be the champion, and implement the best ideas to improve your program, project, or product.

Timing

Design and Construction

VM may be applied at several stages in design development. However, the early application of VM yields the best results. Successful applications on construction projects include the following:

Design-Bid-Build Procurement Method, in which you perform VM at the:

- Concept development stage.
- 25–35% design completion stage.
- 65–75% design completion stage.

Design-Build Procurement Method, in which you perform VM on the:

- Request for proposal documents.
- Design/build team proposals prior to team selection.
- Design/build team project early submittals.

Manufacturing

When VM is applied to a new concept in the manufacturing industry, it is referred to as VE. When VM is applied to an existing product, it is typically referred to as VA.

Manufacturing and VE

- Design concept phase (preproduction, pretooling, prevalidation, precustomer approval)

Manufacturing and VA (performed on the manufactured product)

- Postproduction (revalidate, retool, obtain customer approval again)

Management Applications

VM may be used to create a new approach to business. For instance, you may use VM to restructure an organization; to reconsider the paperwork trail of a patient as he/she enters the hospital emergency room and moves through the hospital's departments; or to analyze the functions and responsibilities of a company's marketing force.

Define the problem you want to solve, involve the decisionmakers and the stakeholders, and use VM to make change.

The results of a VM study are dependent on:

- Project cost—the greater the cost, the greater the potential savings.
- Project complexity.
- The stage of design completion or stage of product or process development.
- The human equation—the need or desire to change dictated by politics, budget, schedule, etc.

The results of a VM study can be evaluated based on:

- Dollar return on VM investment.
- Schedule improvement.
- Better collaboration or communication among owner, designer, and user.
- Validation of the project.
- Improved performance and quality.
- Number of patents developed.
- Sustainability improvements.

Chapter 4

Conducting a VM Workshop

Workshop Site

No matter what application of VM is being planned, an important factor for a successful event is choosing the proper location for the workshop. When determining the location for a VM workshop, consider various factors, such as the ease of reviewing the facility and operations, minimizing travel expenses, and minimizing distraction to the team members during the workshop.

There is an obvious advantage to holding the manufacturing product or process workshop at the site of the manufacturing facility where access to the production floor is easy. The disadvantage, however, is that access to the engineers responsible for the day-to-day activity is also easy—they may be pulled out of the workshop whenever a production issue or problem arises, thus disrupting the flow of the workshop activities. Therefore, in some cases, it is more productive to hold the workshop at a location close to, but not physically at, the manufacturing site.

For a VM workshop for a construction project, there are certain advantages to conducting the workshop close to or at the project site, enabling a formal site visit and access to maintenance and operations staff. This is especially true of a rehabilitation/renovation project.

In all cases, a strong VM facilitator will be required to minimize distraction. But access, travel, and distraction are the factors that need to be considered before a work-shop location is chosen.

Workshop Room Environment

Choosing the proper workshop room environment is also important to the success of the VM study. Several items should be considered:

- Size of space:
  - Seating room for team and guests.
  - Wall space for hanging worksheets and exhibits.
  - Extra table space for exhibits and products.
- Location of space in the facility or manufacturing plant.
- Natural lighting/windows.
- Temperature control.
- Computer/internet access.
- Teleconference capability.

Choose a room that is large enough to easily accommodate the VM team members, the owner, the user, the designer, and other visitors when seated at tables. In addition, for manufacturing studies, it is helpful to have extra tables available in the room to display the products or projects being studied as well as any competitive products or projects that will be analyzed during the workshop. Choose a room where charts, graphs, drawings, and other required documentation may be hung on the walls so the team can reference these documents throughout the VM effort.

Room location can also be critical to the VM team's effectiveness if a manufacturing product or process is the workshop focus. If the workshop is held at the manufacturing site, choose a room that is relatively quiet where the shop noise will not distract the team, yet close enough that the team can tour the plant easily when questions arise. If possible, tour the plant during the workshop's information phase so the team members become familiar with the project being studied.

It is the VM facilitator's responsibility to ensure that the room has the space and location to properly accommodate the study team and management team. The actual arrangement of the room may be flexible based on the type of study, table shape and size, and room shape. Generally, however, tables arranged at a forty-five degree angle to the front of the room are useful because the team members can easily see information projected on a screen or wall and face each other. In all cases, it is useful to have natural lighting/windows, computer/internet access, and temperature control. It is the facilitator's responsibility to arrange the room prior to the workshop to accommodate the group and visitors.

Required Materials and Logistics

In order to properly facilitate a VM study, materials and logistical support are required, including:

- Computer.
- Projector and screen.
- Flip chart, stand and pads, markers.
- Tape and thumb tacks.
- Sticky notes.
- Extension cords.

If they are not available, the VM facilitator will provide these items. Inquire what will be allowed on the walls of the workshop room so the paint or wall coverings are not damaged.

Facilitation Skills

A certified value professional should be chosen to facilitate a VM workshop since he/she has the training and experience to manage the team, implement the methodology, and maximize the benefits to the client and customers. During the preworkshop coordination meeting, the team leader will establish the workshop guidelines, which may include items such as:

- Requiring workshop attendance at agreed-upon times (some team members' participation may not be necessary for the full workshop).

- Requesting that nonworkshop related e-mail, internet, and phone usage occur during breaks and lunch.

- Eliciting participation and consensus from all team members.

- Maintaining the agenda and being punctual about starting times.

- Encouraging the team members to contribute to the preparation of the management presentation and participate in the presentation of results.

The VM facilitator should follow each step of VM. The effectiveness of the study will be enhanced if each phase is implemented. Activities and tools that should be included in a VM study include:

- Reviewing competitive products, processes, or projects for comparative purposes.

- Reviewing other value models, such as time study, cost, life-cycle cost, space, quality, risk, and sustainability models.

- Performing function analysis.

- Preparing FAST Diagrams.

- Creating a cost/function diagram or similar relational technique.
- Using brainstorming or other creative techniques.
- Doing the following during the creative phase:
  - Allowing discussion to clarify an idea not understood by the team.
  - Deferring judgment of ideas to the evaluation phase.
  - Encouraging each team member to participate in generating ideas.
  - Encouraging piggybacking of ideas already mentioned.
  - Limiting domination or control by any one team member.
  - Emphasizing that there are no bad ideas and all ideas are important.
  - Conducting the creative phase "by function" as established by the cost/function priorities or other function-based value models.
- Developing a complete business case during the workshop.
- Conducting a session presenting the results for management and the decisionmakers.

If these guidelines are followed, the team will achieve the goals of the workshop and true "value" will be recognized as the team presents its finding to the project stakeholders at the conclusion of the workshop.

For more information on facilitation tools and techniques, see *Facilitation at a Glance!*

Chapter 5

Team Member Selection and Team Building

Coming together is a beginning, keeping together is progress, and working together is success.
—Henry Ford

Selecting the VM Team

Selecting the team members for any VM workshop is an essential ingredient for success.

Knowing and understanding candidates' education, skills, and experiences will assist in developing the multidisciplinary skills, experiences, knowledge, and personalities that spell success. Teaching and following the VM Job Plan gives the team all the necessary tools during the workshop.

Professionals from several different areas of expertise should be considered when structuring a VM team; value is not any one group's responsibility but is shared by all functional groups within the company or organization. The technical knowledge required for the team should be dictated by the project selected.

Normally, five to seven people work well in one VM team. With fewer than five people on a team, there may be insufficient expertise to analyze the project. Remember that while five to seven people work well on a team, the VM study may be composed of multiple teams working together to accomplish the goals and objectives of the study.

These are the general rules for selecting the VM team:

- Define the disciplines that will be required for the workshop and discuss/concur with the project owner. A typical mix of disciplines for different types of projects is shown on page 22.

- Identify candidates to fill those disciplines. These may be from the project team, the larger organization, or independent consultants.

- Analyze each candidate's capabilities, education, training, experience, and personality. Remember that you want open-minded, creative people on your teams. Also remember that the VM team members' qualifications should be equal to or greater than those of the project/design team members to ensure professionalism.

- Speak to the candidates directly to ensure that they can commit the appropriate time to the project based on the project's schedule and specific activities—the preworkshop coordination meeting, VM workshop, and postworkshop meetings.

- Discuss final team member selection with the project owner so he/she is also committed to this team.

- Communicate with all of the candidates once final team member selection has occurred so they can finalize their schedules or move on to other projects.

On projects in which the team will comprise players from the project's organization, some value practitioners like to include a "wild card" team member. This is someone who has experience but is not intimately familiar with the project under study. This person can be valuable since he/she has not lived with the methods or design concepts of the project and is free to innovate and explore new opportunities and ideas.

Typical Disciplines for Different Types of Projects

Required Discipline	Construction	Product Design	Manufacturing Process	Administrative Process	Service Organization
Project Manager	X	X		X	X
Designer/Architect	X	X			
Specialty Engineer, i.e., Civil, Electrical, Structural, Industrial	X		X		
Process Engineer		X	X	X	X
Manufacturing		X	X	X	X
Facilities Manager	X	X	X	X	X
Owner/Customer	X	X	X	X	X
Contractor	X				
Supplier/Builder	X	X	X	X	X
Quality/Inspector	X	X	X		
Marketing/Sales		X			X
Financial Manager	X	X		X	X
Cost/Estimator	X	X	X	X	X
Other—depending on project	X	X	X	X	X

Team Building

Value practitioners can learn much about team building from successful sports teams. It is often said in the "winner's circle" that a team won because the members believe in themselves and each other, because they all get along, because they have a special chemistry, and even because they are like a family to each other. Practitioners can build on this knowledge and use it in a practical way in VM workshops. We all want our teams to be in the "winner's circle," so how does a VM team accomplish this mentality in one or two weeks when sports teams have several months or years to achieve it?

A team begins as a group of people having the same objectives and expectations. The successful completion of the task supersedes any individual team member's personal aspirations. To optimize the chances for success, team development and team building activities are useful.

For a team to survive and be successful it must have an achievable goal and objective. This step, which may be accomplished at a preworkshop meeting, starts before the team members are selected and ends with all team members knowing, understanding, and committing to that goal and objective. Teams without a clear and concise goal and objective may find it difficult to succeed. Indeed, how would they know if they had? By having clear, specific goals and objectives, team members know exactly what they must do.

The team may write its goal and objective while considering the needs of the owner, customer, or corporate leadership. The team thus agrees on the goal and objective and commits to achieving them. This up-front commitment fosters success. Each team member must identify with the team objective. In a way, the team objective becomes personal.

Refer to The Memory Jogger™ series of pocket guides for

team building ideas. Have several different team building exercises available to use, and select the one that is most appropriate for the given situation. The team building output is a cohesive body focused on a specific task with a unified commitment to achieve that task.

Chapter 6

The Value Methodology Job Plan

A system for use when better than normal results are needed. —Lawrence D. Miles

Application of the VM Job Plan

The process for applying VM is referred to as the VM Job Plan, which consists of the following three efforts:

- Preworkshop activities (also referred to as the prestudy step).

- VM workshop activities (also referred to as the value study step).

- Postworkshop activities (also referred to as the poststudy step).

> The preworkshop, VM workshop, and postworkshop activities are collectively referred to as the VM study.

As shown in the figure on page 26, the VM Job Plan is broken down into specific steps, which are used to effectively analyze a product or service in order to develop the maximum number of alternatives to achieve the product's or service's required functions. Adherence to this plan will assure maximum benefits while offering greater flexibility.

The Value Methodology Job Plan

PRESTUDY

Collect User/Customer Attitudes
Complete Data File
Determine Evaluation Factors
Scope the StudyBuild Data Models
Determine Team Composition

VALUE STUDY

Information Phase
Complete Data Package
Modify Scope
Function Analysis Phase
Identify Functions
Classify Functions
Develop Function Models
Establish Function Worth
Cost Functions
Establish Value Index
Select Functions for Study
Creative Phase
Create Quantity of Ideas by Function
Evaluation Phase
Rank and Rate Alternative Ideas
Select Ideas for Development
Development Phase
Conduct Benefit Analysis
Complete Technical Data Package
Create Implementation Plan
Prepare Final Proposals
Presentation Phase
Present Oral Report
Prepare Written Report

Obtain Commitments for Implementation

POSTSTUDY

Complete Changes
Implement Changes
Monitor Status

The second step—the VM workshop—consists of the following six phases, which are conducted sequentially:

1. **Information phase.**
2. **Function analysis phase.**
3. **Creative phase.**
4. **Evaluation phase.**
5. **Development phase.**
6. **Presentation phase.**

At the owner/stakeholder's request, the following two phases are frequently included:

- Implementation phase.
- Follow-up phase.

Why use the VM Job Plan?

Use the VM Job Plan to systematically focus a value improvement study and ensure its essential steps are implemented.

How is it unique?

The VM Job Plan is a scientific method of problem solving with two special features:

- The function analysis phase.
- The creative and evaluation phases—a clear separation between generating creative ideas and judging their validity and ability to be implemented.

Preworkshop Activities

Information Phase

The preworkshop activities of any VM study are as important as the actual workshop. If the organization, planning, and information are not properly defined and systematically collected, it will be difficult for the VM team to attain the goals and objectives of the effort. Employ a certified value specialist to organize, plan, and set guidelines for the necessary information to be gathered prior to conducting the VM study to maximize the benefits expected from VM.

Conduct a preworkshop meeting about two weeks prior to the scheduled workshop to ensure that all of the required documentation and items on the preworkshop checklist are compiled or completed. If the required information is not available before the workshop, it will be difficult to secure it during the workshop. In addition, much of this information will be distributed to each team member prior to the start of the workshop so that each participant understands the project and has the time to develop questions about it.

During the VM workshop planning process, assess the size and composition of the study team. Teams of five to seven members excel. Create multidisciplinary teams to incorporate the knowledge required to cover the issues and objectives of the project being studied.

For some projects, it is desirable to have a team on which each member is a project stakeholder; that way every person has a vested interest in improving the product, process, or project and an inclination to contribute with a positive, enthusiastic attitude. On other projects, it is useful to have a multidisciplinary team that is completely independent of the stakeholder team. In a third scenario, a team comprising the project stakeholder and independent specialists may be the most useful approach to achieve success. The project owner and the VM facilitator should discuss the team composition and determine which of the three approaches will work for the application at hand.

No matter which team grouping is selected, it is important that the team members:

- Are experienced in their fields of practice, e.g., engineering, architecture, operations, manufacturing, or construction.
- Are inquisitive and open to new ideas.
- Promote the ideas of others.
- Demonstrate respect for the concepts generated by others.
- Participate.

The VM team composition depends on several factors, including:

- The type of project being studied, i.e., manufactured product or process, construction project, or management process.
- The stage of completion of the project.
- The value of the project.

While teams generally work best in groups of five to seven people, it is not uncommon to conduct a workshop with multiple teams. These teams may be created based on disciplines or major project components. An example might be the VM study of a light rail transit project in which four teams of five to seven people each concentrate on the topics of alignment (including track work, civil work, and utilities), structures (including elevated, at grade, and below grade), architecture (including signage, lighting, and art), and constructability (including cost, construction, and schedule). The VM team is never limited to a certain number of people. It is dependant on many factors, and these should be carefully considered when discussing the composition with the project manager.

TEAM: See the section on team selection.

A manufactured product or process design VM workshop may include these members:

- Operational/launch program manager.
- Product/application engineer.
- Manufacturing/process engineer.
- Quality engineer.
- Purchasing representative.
- Customer/sales/marketing representative.
- Finance/cost estimating representative.
- Outside supplier or global engineering representative.
- VM facilitator.

A construction project VM workshop may include these members:

- Architect.
- Engineer—disciplines depend on project being reviewed, e.g., civil, structural, mechanical, electrical, geotechnical, sanitary, environmental, etc.
- Cost estimator.
- Construction specialist.
- Operations and maintenance specialist.
- Owner.
- Design team members.
- VM facilitator.

The selection and attendance of the team members is critical to the successful outcome of the event. When the team members participate in the preworkshop meeting and the VM workshop, the effectiveness and impact of the study may increase since consensus and technically viable and implementable VM ideas are generated for the stakeholders to consider.

PURPOSE: Questions such as, "What is the purpose of this study?" "What does the customer want?" and "What benefit will this study bring to the user?" are important for all of the study team members and supporting management team to answer and agree upon at the preworkshop meeting. Once there is consensus on these items, the scope of the workshop can be developed and finalized by those attending the preworkshop meeting.

SCOPE: When determining the project scope, a variety of questions must be answered, such as, "What are the boundaries of the study?" and "What will be considered and what will not be considered?" The entire VM study team and the supporting management team must agree on the answers to these questions prior to the workshop so the proper information is gathered and the focus of the workshop well understood by all involved. This will ensure that, upon completion of the VM study, everyone will be satisfied that the specific problem being studied is properly addressed.

Information Needed

A checklist is a simple way to ensure that the VM team is prepared for its effort during the workshop. The following three checklists are variations based on the application. Use them and tailor them to your project's needs.

For each of the following checklists, the agenda and details concerning logistics, support items, and appropriate project documents should be provided to the team members in advance of the workshop so they may make arrangements, as necessary, and be prepared for the first day of the workshop.

One copy of all project materials should be available at the workshop. The VM facilitator should organize and inform the management team of the review.

Manufactured Product Preworkshop Checklist

- Agenda, including:
  - Dates
  - Times
  - Location
  - Participants
  - Scheduled activities—the VM job plan
  - Management review time, date, and participants
  - Meals—lunch and dinner arrangements, as appropriate
- Logistics, including:
  - Meeting space
  - Food
  - Lodging
  - Local transportation
  - Maps, as necessary
  - Support
- Laptop computer
- Projector
- Flip chart easel and pads
- Customer (requirements) statement of work (legal customer agreement)

- Costed bill of materials with material and processing information
- Samples components (assembled and unassembled)
- Assembly and all component drawings
- Design Failure Mode and Effect Analysis (DFMEA) for product being studied
- Competitive analysis (documentation and actual parts)
- Customer wants
- Product drawings
- Packaging
- Warranty information
- Project and prototype parts
- Competitive parts
- Test and qualification requirements
- Repair, scrap, and reoperation information
- General and Administrative and overhead costs
- Product cost breakdown

Manufacturing Process Preworkshop Checklist

- Agenda, including:
  - Dates
  - Times
  - Location
  - Participants
  - Scheduled activities—the VM job plan
  - Management review time, date, and participants

- Meals—lunch/dinner arrangements, as appropriate
- Logistics, including:
  - Meeting space
  - Food
  - Lodging
  - Local transportation
  - Maps, as necessary
  - Support
- Laptop computer
- Projector
- Flip chart easel and pads
- Process operations or work instructions per operation with visuals
- Process tool and labor routing worksheets
- Tooling and maintenance reports (equipment up-time, etc.)
- Process flow diagrams (and store/move/inspect/wait/process time study)
- DFMEA
- Competitive and alternative process opportunities
- Process flow diagram
- Value stream map
- Production volumes
- Forecast volumes
- Inventory volumes
- Storage methods and shelf life
- Distribution methods

©2008 GOAL/QPC

Construction Project Preworkshop Checklist

- Agenda, including:
  - Dates
  - Times
  - Location
  - Participants
  - Scheduled activities—the VM job plan
  - Management review time, date, and participants
  - Meals—lunch/dinner arrangements, as appropriate
- Logistics, including:
  - Meeting space
  - Food
  - Lodging
  - Local transportation
  - Maps, as necessary
  - Support
- Laptop computer
- Projector
- Flip chart easel and pads
- Project or program
- Basis of design
- Budget development documents
- Drawings for the level of design under study
- Outline or design specifications
- Definition of major system and subsystems including structural, architectural, mechanical, electrical, site work, and utilities

- Plot plan, topography, and site planning, including photos
- Space analysis
- Computations
- Codes and criteria
- Verification of utility (power, sewer, gas) available for new site
- Geotechnical/soils reports with response for foundation design (on drawings)
- Cost estimate
- Critical Path Method (CPM) schedule
- Economic data, budget constraints, discount rates, and use life
- Special systems or requirements
- Project constraints
- Regulatory requirements
- Commitments made to the public

Secure the information noted in the previous checklists prior to the VM workshop, so the study team is well on its way to meeting the owner's project value objectives. The effort spent in this preworkshop stage may determine the success of the VM study. Complete the preparation work prior to the workshop to ensure the maximum effectiveness of VM.

> PROJECT DATA: If the required information is not gathered before the workshop, it will be difficult to secure the information during the actual workshop, potentially hampering the team, their productivity, and the results.

Facilitator Preparation

In addition to coordinating the logistics, team structure, purpose, and scope of the VM workshop with the project stakeholders, the facilitator will also prepare other project documents prior to the VM workshop. These include:

- Models for cost, space, energy, and work break-down
- Value stream maps and flow charts

Chapter 7

The Value Methodology Job Plan: Workshop Activities

Information Phase

> *Good information is both truthful and relevant.*
> —Carlos Fallon

The information phase continues at the beginning of the VM workshop as its first activity.

- **Management address**—Management opens the workshop and welcomes the team, stressing the importance of the workshop's outcome to the organization and asking for a presentation of results at the conclusion of the workshop.

- **Project overview**—The project designer, project manager, marketing representative, or other appropriate project representatives present the project background, information, and constraints and provide points of contact and telephone numbers for use by the VM team during the workshop.

- **Evaluation of data gathered**—In some applications, such as a design/construction VM study, the VM team has received and reviewed the project documents prior to the VM workshop. In other applications, the team sees the project documents for the first time on the first day of the workshop. In all cases, the team reviews the information collected to date, determines what additional information they might need, and collects that information by requesting it after the project overview. Then the team tours the project site, plant, operations, or whatever location is required so that they can see the project in use, in production, or in operation.

Function Analysis Phase

All cost is for function. People want to eat fish, not bait hook.—Lawrence D. Miles

Purpose

The purpose of the function analysis phase is to identify the greatest opportunities for the improvement of value.

Questions

Answer these questions about the subject of the VM study:

- What does it do?
- What is the value of the function?
- What does it need to do?

Procedures

Define each function being performed by the study subject. To do this, state what a product or process must do to make it work and sell. For each function, use an active verb and a measurable noun.

- **Basic and supporting functions**—Most study subjects have many functions that will be classified during the workshop as basic or supporting functions.

- **Simple words**—To state what something does in two words is sometimes difficult, but it helps to simplify terminology and create better understanding. A process is designed to "shape material." A material procedure is designed to "locate material." Simple statements such as these ensure clarity of thought and communication with little confusion of meaning. When choosing the words that define a function, make them as broad and generic as possible. Do not select words that predetermine a single way that the function should be performed.

- **Active verbs**—Avoid the use of the words "provide," "allow," and "facilitate." Avoid using verbs that end with -ize. Often when one of these verbs is used, the function can be reworded to become correct by making the noun a verb and finding a new noun. For example, "provide support" becomes "support weight."

- **Number**—It is common to make the verb plural, i.e., "supports weight" or "resists corrosion," but there is no need to do this.

- **Measurable nouns**—Always strive for a measurable noun. This will take time and patience. Do not use the name of a component part that is included in the project under study.

- **Verb/noun lists**—See the list of typical verbs and nouns on pages 41 and 42.

- **Operations versus functions**—Do not use operations or activities as functions. Even seasoned value specialists fall into the trap of confusing functions with operations, or the actions that a device performs as a result of a function. This is especially true in studying a process. For example, "drill hole" is an operation, "make opening" is a function. In a mousetrap, "swing striker" is an action that the mouse trap performs as a result of the functions "release energy" and "deliver impact."

List of Typical Verbs and Nouns

Products

Verbs		Nouns	
absorb	generate	access	friction
access	guide	air	heat
actuate	improve	appearance	impact
allow	increase	bending	light
apply	isolate	circuit	mass
attach	limit	climate	material
attract	maintain	cold	moisture
circulate	pivot	comfort	motion
conduct	position	component	noise
connect	prevent	corrosion	occupant
contain	protect	current	parts
control	provide	deflection	path
convert	reduce	dirt	performance
create	regulate	drag	pressure
decrease	resist	energy	stability
direct	rotate	entry	surface
enclose	seal	environment	torque
enhance	sense	flow	travel
extend	support	fluid	vibration
facilitate	transmit	force	weight

Processes

Verbs		Nouns	
allow	join	alignment	flash
apply	load	assembly	gauge
assemble	maintain	burr	gas
assure	make	casting	heat
blend	move	cause	hole
clean	position	cleanliness	inventory
control	prevent	cold	length
convert	protect	component	locator
create	provide	container	machine
decrease	receive	correction	material
deliver	release	damage	mold
facilitate	remove	defect	operation
fasten	repair	device	part
fill	rotate	die	priority
finish	seal	dimension	schedule
form	store	dirt	shape
identify	supply	environment	surface
improve	thread	equipment	tool
increase	transport	finish	uniformity
inspect	verify	fixture	waste

Continued on next page

List of Typical Verbs and Nouns (continued)

Procedures

Verbs		Nouns	
allocate	identify	alternative	material
allow	improve	awareness	option
analyze	increase	concept	order
audit	inform	control	part
authorize	maintain	coordination	performance
certify	measure	criteria	personnel
compile	monitor	data	plan
confirm	obtain	decision	priority
copy	organize	design	process
create	procure	deviation	record
decrease	protect	direction	regulation
develop	provide	documentation	request
distribute	receive	facility	resource
enter	reconcile	funds	schedule
establish	record	goal	shipment
evaluate	report	history	source
facilitate	set	information	staff
forecast	specify	instruction	standard
generate	test	inventory	status
guide	transmit	limit	trend

Projects

Verbs		Nouns	
absorb	heat	air	material
alter	illuminate	appearance	objects
amplify	impede	balance	oxidation
change	improve	beauty	parking
circulate	increase	color	people
collect	induce	communication	power
condition	insulate	compression	preparation
conduct	interrupt	convenience	prestige
connect	modulate	current	protection
contain	prevent	ego	radiation
control	protect	enclosure	sheer
convey	provide	energy	sound
cool	rectify	environment	space
create	reduce	features	structure
distribute	reflect	feeling	style
emit	repel	fire	symmetry
enclose	resist	flow	temperature
enjoy	separate	fluids	tension
establish	shield	force	texture
exclude	smell	form	tone
extinguish	support	heat	torque
feel	taste	image	utilities
filter	think	landscape	view
finish	transmit	light	voltage
generate	ventilate	load	weight

- **Combining functions**—Often component parts perform holding, supporting, or positioning functions like "hold bearing" or "position washer." It is best to combine all these hold, support, and position functions into a single function, such as "hold components." By doing this the team will better see how much cost is going into these functions. Brainstorming with this generic function will lead to many ideas. During evaluation, the ideas can be sorted back into the actual design area to which they can be applied.

- **Understanding multiple use functions**—Find out how something is used. A screwdriver whose designed function is to "transfer torque" might be used to "pry lid" off a can of paint and then to "stir paint." A standard door whose designed function is to "control opening" might be used to "screen occupant" in a dressing room.

When you have generated as many functions as you can, start a function worksheet by placing the functions you do have in the center box as shown in the table on page 44. Then ask why and how each function is achieved and place the verb/noun answers in the left and right boxes respectively. Repeat this activity by placing the new functions in the center box and questioning them. (Another example of a function analysis worksheet is depicted in the table on page 45.)

Create a FAST diagram to identify additional missing functions and to organize them in order to classify them.

Refer to Appendix A, the FAST section
of this pocket guide.

Function Worksheet

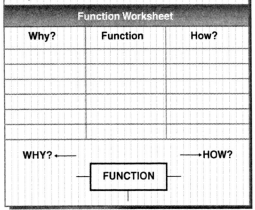

First, brainstorm functions of the item and place them in the center box.

Second, ask how each function is performed and place that answer in the right column.

Third ask why each function is performed and place that answer in the left column.

Finally, place all the answers in the center and continue to ask questions.

Function Worksheet

Why?	Function	How?

WHY? ←——— ———→HOW?

FUNCTION

Classify the functions. The major function classifications are basic functions and secondary functions. A basic function is the primary purpose or most important action performed by a product, process, or service.

The basic function must always exist, although methods or designs to achieve it may vary.

©2008 GOAL/QPC

Function Analysis and Cost-Worth

PROJECT: ____

NO.	ELEMENT	VERB	NOUN	KIND	COST (000)	WORTH (000)	COMMENTS

Function defined as: Action Verb
Measurable
Noun

Kind: B = Basic
S = Secondary
RS = Required Secondary

HO = Higher Order
LO = Lower Order

Cost/Worth Ratio =
(Total Cost ÷ Basic Worth)

A secondary function is a function that supports the basic function and results from the specific design approach used to perform the basic function. The VM team's goal is to ultimately reduce or eliminate as many secondary functions as possible.

The three types of secondary functions

1. **Required secondary functions are those functions that are necessary in a product or project to perform the basic function.** For example, both a battery-operated flashlight and a kerosene lantern perform the basic function of producing light. A required secondary function, however, in one is to "conduct current" while the equivalent secondary function in the other is to "conduct fluid."

2. **Aesthetic secondary functions are those functions that add beauty or decor to the product or project and are generally associated with "sell functions."** For example, the colors of paint available for a car could be an aesthetic secondary function.

> An aesthetic function can sometimes be a basic function when it becomes one of the primary purposes of the product or project.

3. **Unwanted secondary functions are those functions that by definition are not wanted while the product is performing the basic or secondary function(s).** In the case of the kerosene lantern, while the basic function of producing light is being performed, an unwanted secondary function is "produce odor."

©2008 GOAL/QPC

Allocate resources to all functions

The most important aspect of function analysis is the determination of cost/function relationships. It is this technique that identifies where unnecessary cost exists within the study item. Note that while not all projects use cost/function relationships, this relationship is the most common. Other projects may have function relationships to time, mass, weight, or even a quality metric. Construction relationships to function can be space, profit, revenue, energy, parameter, or even a Leadership in Energy and Environmental Design (LEED) metric. The common denominator in all of these relationships is function.

A cost/function worksheet is used to develop this aspect of function analysis (see the table on page 48).

1. **Start by listing all functions between the scope lines across the top of the form.**

2. **List the parts or major sub-assemblies down the left-hand side of the form with the associated incremental costs.**

3. **Check off which function(s) are affected by each part or sub-assembly.**

4. **Determine how much of the cost of each part or sub-assembly belongs to each function.**

5. **Add all columns vertically to determine how much cost is allocated to each function.**

See the Function Analysis and Cost-Worth table on page 45 for an example of how to define functions and costs for other applications, such as construction or process projects.

Cost/Function Worksheet

Project: Hospital Laboratory Testing Process

Function Number		1	42
	Time (Minutes)	Obtain Data	Control Flow
STAFF MEMBER/ACTIVITY			
Physician			
Write order at nurse station	2		
Place order in order box	1		1
Clerk			
Collect orders, bring to central station	1		1
Collect orders take to lab	5		3
Distribute labels with bottles to central station	2		1
Sort bottles, labels	5		1
Distribute bottles, labels to nurse	5		
Bring specimens to central station	2		2
Bring specimens to lab	5		5
Deliver results to central station	10		10
Deliver results to nurse station	5		
Technician			
Enter order on computer	10		
Generate labels with computer	5		
Perform test	5	5	
Enter results on computer	2		
Print out test data	5		
Nurse			
Pick up bottles, labels, take to patient	5		
Take specimen, affix label	2		
Return specimen to nurse station	2		2
File results in patient record	10	2	2
Order (Waiting)	120		
Specimen (Waiting)	40		40
TOTAL COSTS STUDIED (Minutes)	249		
TOTAL FUNCTION COST (Minutes)	>>>	7	68
COST OF FUNCTION AS % OF TOTAL COST		3%	27%

Determine the worth of each function

Function worth is the lowest cost to perform the function without regard to criteria or code.

How do you determine function worth? Many methods may be used, including:

- A historical database.
- Benchmarking data.
- VM team member experience.
- Cost estimator experience/expertise.
- The lowest cost of an alternate way to perform the function.
- The cost of another product that performs the same function.
- Costing software.
- Cost reference books.
- A target based on historical savings from past VM efforts.
- A method based upon the budget.

> The worth of secondary functions is often viewed as zero because they only exist to support the basic function. For example, the worth of a valve to control flow is zero because the valve would not exist in an all-air electric heating system.

Calculate value indexes

The value index is a relationship of function worth (FW) to function cost (FC).

$$\text{Value Index} = \frac{\text{Function Worth}}{\text{Function Cost}}$$

Note that you may find this ratio reversed to read

$$\text{Value Index} = \frac{\text{Function Cost}}{\text{Function Worth}}$$

Use either ratio. The SAVE International Certification Board accepts both. In most cases, the value index should be determined at the system level or product level. Only when extensive cost detail is available can the value index be used at functional levels. In this case, only the predominant cost drivers (functions) are used. The purpose of the value index is to help a VM team to identify areas of opportunity to channel their creative energy.

Cost/function relationships provide direction to the team by illustrating the area(s) of the project with the greatest opportunity for cost and value improvement. In other words, at this point, the team is able to identify which functions are not providing good value. Having completed this analysis, the team is ready to focus on specific functions and develop additional alternatives. They are ready for the second phase of the VM Job Plan and the third phase of the VM Workshop, the creative phase.

Refer to Appendix A of this guide for additional techniques for how to map functions.

Creative Phase

Mind tuning is an essential step in problem solving.—Lawrence D. Miles

Purpose

The purpose of the creative phase is to generate a large quantity of ideas or alternatives that can perform the basic functions identified from the previous phase.

Questions

Answer these questions:

- What other ideas will perform the function?
- What else will do the job?
- Does the job need to be done at all?

Procedures

Establish an open-minded atmosphere for creativity. Set ground rules. Set aside a specific time and place for the generation of ideas. Establish a significant goal for the number of ideas. Disallow comment on each idea as it is expressed, not even a snicker.

Brainstorming is the most common technique used to generate ideas during a value study. To brainstorm:

- Look for a large number of ideas.
- Do not worry about the quality of ideas.
- Defer all judgment of ideas until the next phase.
- Promote combining old ideas with new ideas.
- Encourage hitchhiking on ideas.

The brainstorming technique works best if everyone in the room is willing and eager to participate. Let all participants clear their minds by first listing those pent-up ideas they have been holding back since the information and function analysis phases. Bring forward all the function alternatives used to determine worth in the function analysis phase. Then list each idea on large flip chart sheets and hang them around the room for all to see as each chart fills up. (The table on page 53 shows another way to document creative ideas.)

If participants are shy about offering ideas or if the range of ideas becomes limited and focused on the existing solution, try the Gordon Technique. In this technique, the leader is the only person who knows the problem, so no one is embarrassed to contribute ideas.

> Here's an example of the Gordon Technique. List alternate ways to "shorten it." When the number of ideas that are offered begin to slow down, place a fake object in the place of the noun, e.g., "shorten pencil." This will focus ideas on a subject and greatly add to the list. Repeat with another fake noun as often as you like. At the end, announce the real function being explored, e.g., "shorten grass." You will have dozens of methods to shorten something that you would not have had on the list had you begun with "shorten grass."

Other creative techniques can be used to generate large quantities of ideas relevant to the study. See *The Creativity Tools Memory Jogger*™ for other creative techniques, one of which is morphological analysis (see the figure on page 54). Morphological analysis forces combinations of ideas that would not normally and systematically be considered—and no one is to blame!

Let the mind incubate and develop more ideas. Allow sufficient time for thinking and reflecting. Don't judge the ideas on the same day they are created! Additional ideas can come in the next day and be added to the list for consideration. Ask for them.

Creative Worksheet

Creative Idea Listing		
Function:		
List ways to provide the function		
Idea No.	**Description**	**Rating**
Rating:	Yes—Investigate; Not Now—consider in the future; Nonsense—discard	
or	5—Great Idea – investigate;	
	4—Good idea, minor disadvantage ….	
	1—Nonsense, discard	

Remember, creativity equals imagination plus inspiration plus illumination!

Evaluation Phase

Unfortunately, most decisions are made on a basis of avoiding or minimizing personal loss.
—Lawrence D. Miles

Purpose

The purpose of the evaluation phase is to judge the ideas generated during the creative phase.

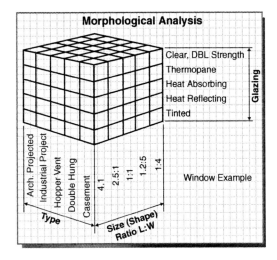

Morphological Analysis

Glazing:
- Clear, DBL Strength
- Thermopane
- Heat Absorbing
- Heat Reflecting
- Tinted

Type:
- Arch. Projected
- Industrial Project
- Hopper Vent
- Double Hung
- Casement

Size (Shape) Ratio L:W:
- 4:1
- 2.5:1
- 1:1
- 1:2.5
- 1:4

Window Example

Questions

Answer these questions about each idea:

- Will the idea achieve the basic function?
- Will required performance and quality be achieved?
- Will the idea improve value?
- Is it readily implementable?
- Are there significant roadblocks to overcome?

Procedure

This phase begins with a large number and many variations of raw ideas and ends with one or more good ideas, which will be further developed and presented for approval.

Classify/rank the ideas

During the creative phase, the VM team was asked to withhold its judgment. During the evaluation phase, the team screens their raw ideas to reduce them to a manageable quantity.

Using the creative worksheet (page 53), on which the team has recorded all the ideas generated individually and collectively, classify or rank each idea. Use a simple formula, such as yes, not now, or no, or use a number system of 1 to 5 in which 5 is a great idea and 1 is nonsense.

Remember, a new idea is a young and tender thing. It can easily be stepped on and discarded. The initial objective here is to protect ideas so they get a fair shot at being evaluated, not to see how many you can discard. At the beginning, it is still not clear to the team how some of these ideas, when combined with others, may lead to an important discovery for a product or process improvement.

As the team classifies ideas, record them on oversized sheets of paper to encourage participation, and use these reminders:

- Consider everything.
- Be reasonable.
- Be fair. The past is not sacred!
- What ideas seem feasible?
- Can any ideas be modified or combined with others?
- Will each idea satisfy the user's needs?

Often additional ideas are generated during this phase. Add them to the brainstorming worksheet and classify them too.

Developing your ideas

After the team has classified or ranked its ideas, they may use one of several methods to develop them. We suggest two methods here.

As Albert Einstein said, "Sometimes the solution presents itself politely and says, 'Here I am!'" While this does frequently happen, you will require one of the two methods to generate alternative proposals.

The Forced Relationships Method

The Forced Relationships Method combines ideas into relationships, some of which will be quite unconventional. It consists of three steps.

1. **Categorize ideas.** Determine three or four (possibly more) categories into which your "yes" ideas logically fall. The exact number of categories and the categories themselves depend on your specific study and the ideas generated. The effort is performed for each function that was brainstormed. It is uncommon to have the same categories for different functions, so do not try to force ideas to fit into predetermined categories.

> The categories for one product study emerged as materials, structures, fasteners, and configurations. In one process study, the categories were moving, storing, fabricating, and inspecting, while in one

procedure study, the categories included collecting, transmitting, auditing, and displaying data. In every case, the categories should emerge naturally from your ideas and should be recorded at the top of the idea categorization worksheet (see sample, below).

Idea Categorization Worksheet

Function:		
Grouping	**Idea No.**	**Description**
Moving	A	
Storing	B	
Fabricating	C	
Inspecting	D	

2. **Cost-rank ideas.** Record the ideas on the idea categorization worksheet (shown above) in cost-ranked order with the lowest cost-ranked idea on top. Only cost-rank the ideas at this point because estimating them would waste your time.

It is usually helpful to prepare a supplemental worksheet for this step. Simply divide a piece of paper into the categories chosen, list the ideas, cost-rank them, and then transfer them to the idea categorization worksheet in sequence.

3. **Combine ideas.** Select the lowest cost-ranked idea from each category and combine them—that is, force a relationship—into a proposal that will perform the function(s) that you brainstormed. Then repeat the process, moving to the next lowest cost-ranked idea in a category and combining it with the lowest cost-ranked ideas in other categories, and so on. Most of these combinations will not fit together because the ideas are mutually exclusive. Other combinations will surprise you by developing proposals that are truly innovative.

The Blast-Create-Refine Method

The Blast-Create-Refine Method is an intriguing option since it employs brainstorming in a developmental manner. It is based on the principle that far more unnecessary costs can be removed by reducing a product, process, or procedure to the functional bare minimum and adding only those features necessary to make it work and sell, than by attempting to remove portions of unnecessary cost from the existing product, process, or procedure. This method requires three steps.

1. **Blast the existing product, process, or procedure from your thinking.** Forget all the equipment, tooling, materials, layouts, formats, shapes, and sizes.

2. **Create or brainstorm a simple, cost-effective way to perform the function and generate the bare minimum of what is needed.**

3. **Refine by adding only those features absolutely necessary to make it work and sell.**

Repeat these steps to generate several different proposals. Your "yes" ideas provide the impetus for creating and refining. This powerful method is a classic case of easier said than done. The key to using the Blast-Create-Refine Method successfully is to oversimplify the function to maximize the use of the team's creativity.

T-Chart ideas

After the team has developed several promising proposals using either the Forced Relationships Method or the Blast-Create-Refine Method, they are ready to move into the next stage of idea evaluation.

Prepare a T-Chart worksheet for each proposal (see the table on page 60). To do this:

1. **List all advantages of the idea in the first column.** For example, first list building the team, then helping to develop the proposal by stimulating additional thought, and last forming a basis for selling the proposal. Generate as many good points about the idea as there are bad points.

> Regardless of the evaluation method used, include the original design as one of the alternatives.

2. **List the disadvantages in the second column.** Be honest. Only rarely are there no disadvantages.

3. **Determine how each disadvantage can be overcome by asking, "How can we make it work?"** Write your answer in the third column opposite the corresponding disadvantage, and cross out the disadvantage.

Do not further consider any idea that does not meet the basic function (minimum required criteria).

4. **List factors and/or attributes against which all ideas will be judged.**

5. **Select the method to be used for evaluation.**

T-Charting Format

Put a dollar value on each idea.
Look for good.

GOOD	BAD

Maximize good.   Minimize bad.

Remember, use your creative ability to build the good and reduce the bad! Then sell your ideas based on their *good points*.

You may find that you need to do some brainstorming to overcome a disadvantage, or you may find it can't be overcome. If it can't, set the proposal aside. You may return to it later and, with a fresh mindset, discover a way to make it work.

When all the disadvantages have been crossed out, you have a viable idea and are ready for the next stage.

> Refer to two other evaluation techniques described
> in this pocket guide: Weighted Evaluation
> (Appendix I) and the tablular method of
> Choosing By Advantages (Appendix L).

Segregate the list of ideas into three groups based on their probable time to implement—that is, those requiring a short time, those needing more evaluation, and those that will take a long time to develop. Then look at the ideas and do the following:

- Evaluate achievement of basic function by comparison.
- Use standards to compare methods, products, and materials.
- Quantify and put a dollar value on ideas, and refine the ideas.
- Predict user or customer response to each idea.

Development Phase

> *Bring roadblocks clearly into the open.*
> —Lawrence D. Miles

Purpose
The purpose of the development phase is to develop specific alternatives for change in order to improve value.

Questions
Answer these questions about each alternative:

- What change is specifically recommended?
- Why is it technically acceptable?

- Why is it financially acceptable?
- What is the cost?
- What are its benefits?
- Are there any trade-offs?
- What is the life cycle cost?
- How long will it take to implement?
- How will it be implemented?
- Who will implement it?

Procedures

Simultaneously develop the value proposal to sell it to two audiences, the technical audience and the business audience—the project stakeholders.

> Prevent surprises. It is a good strategy to discuss the value ideas with the decision makers or their advisors prior to presenting them as formal recommendations. Set aside specific times in the workshop session to do this. Communication with the stakeholders will enable the team to get feedback on the possible pitfalls and objections and, conversely, may generate even better refinements to the concept. Maintain the dialogue with the decision makers to incorporate improvements and modifications and to develop presentation materials that address concerns directly.

Technical case

The technical audience includes design, engineering, manufacturing, production, distribution, warehousing, and maintenance specialists. In order to develop and present the technical case to its best advantage, do the following:

- Compare the proposed idea to the current solution to explain how the idea will provide required functions while performing at or above requirements for reliability, mean time between failure, operability, durability, and maintainability.

- Contact vendors and specialists for supporting information regarding the new idea. Investigate new methods and materials for the new idea.

- Prepare the written value proposal describing the original design and the proposed alternative for change.

- Be specific and detailed as to what changes are recommended.

- Be specific as to the scope of the change.

- List the advantages and disadvantages of the change.

Anticipate and mitigate the roadblocks, concerns, or objections the technical audience will have by specifically demonstrating how the new idea is a better value than the original design. Some reasons for the value improvement may include the fact that the value alternative may lower the initial or life cycle cost, increase the rate of production, improve the schedule or constructibility, or mitigate or eliminate major areas of risk. This is the marketing component of VM and the phase of the Job Plan in which the team will influence implementation decisions. Be concise and to the point regarding why this alternative is both technically feasible and implementable. Sell the change with specific information about how it will improve the process, product, project, or service.

Business case

The business audience includes management, financial, marketing, and customer representatives. In order to develop and present the business case to its best advantage, do the following:

- Estimate the initial cost benefit of the proposed idea.

- Determine the break-even point at which the new idea begins to cost less than the original solution. If F = fixed cost, V = variable cost, and X = the break-even quantity, then $X = (F2 - F1) / (V1 - V2)$.

- In a manufacturing study, know the current production volume and in-stock inventory, and define how you will deal with that stock and phase in the new idea.

- Calculate the life cycle cost (LCC) savings of the proposed idea in comparison to the original solution. LCC savings are an important user benefit that normally mean less maintenance and operating cost during use, which equates to a customer concept of a higher quality product.

> See the LCC technique in Appendix K.

- Estimate the implementation cost of the new idea in terms of design changes, retooling, testing, and other overhead elements that drive the total cost of the project.

- Estimate the cost and benefit of retrofitting existing products or equipment as a separate economic decision and recommendation.

- Determine the return on investment (ROI) and/or probable new market share for the idea.

- Indicate specifically what must be changed—which design, what detail, what specification paragraph, what part number, etc.

- Develop the wording for each changed document or new sketch needed.

- If testing is required, minimize risk and expense by suggesting a testing plan that phases in the tests to provide intermediate assurance of performance before continuing.

- Indicate who should make each change that is required to fully implement the idea.

- Indicate when the change should be made and take effect to maximize its benefit in coordination with the ongoing development, production, or construction schedule for the item.

- Draft internal implementing orders to the various departments or the design team approving the change and assigning implementation responsibility and deadlines. Have these orders signed by management.

Again, anticipate roadblocks and mitigate objections in advance. List the other intangible user benefits to be gained from the idea, e.g., simplicity, style, appearance, handling, availability, weight, selection, convenience, and so on. Develop an implementation (action) plan that is both specific and practical to achieve.

Once the VM team has prepared the technical and business cases for the value proposals, the VM team members will finalize the VM proposals. The VM proposals will then be submitted to the project owner and stakeholders and will include information, such as:

- Technical description(s) of the original design concept and the proposed change.

- The advantages and disadvantages of the change.

- Any discussion that mitigates the disadvantages and demonstrates why this proposal offers better value than the original design.
- Sketches of the change.
- Computations/calculations as appropriate.
- A detailed cost estimate of the original and proposal change.
- The cost to implement.
- The life cycle cost benefits.
- A proposed schedule for implementing the change.
- An implementation plan for making the change.

One example of a VM worksheet is shown on page 67.

Presentation Phase

Feelings always influence and often control decisions.—Lawrence D. Miles

Purpose

The purpose of the presentation phase is to sell your ideas!

Questions

Answer these questions about each value alternative:

- What is the specific change recommended?
- How does it perform all required functions?
- Is the change timely?
- Will the change meet the schedule?

Value Engineering Alternative

PROJECT:		ALTERNATIVE NO:	
DESCRIPTION:		SHEET NO:	

ORIGINAL DESIGN:

ALTERNATIVE:

ADVANTAGES: | **DISADVANTAGES:**

DISCUSSION:

COST SUMMARY	INITIAL COST	PRESENT WORTH RECURRING COSTS	PRESENT WORTH LIFE CYCLE COSTS
ORIGINAL DESIGN	$		$
ALTERNATIVE	$		$
SAVINGS (Original minus Alternative)	$		$

- What financial benefits will the change achieve?
- What intangible benefits will be gained by implementation?

Procedures

The team will prepare its presentation of results. While the presentation of a change will be in writing, it is the oral presentation that is necessary to clinch the implementation decision. Use the written report as the basis to make an outline of your oral presentation, as shown in the table on page 69.

Prepare visual aids from your sketches.

> Preparing your presentation as a slide show makes you think it out in advance and ensures that you cover all the material needed.

Schedule a formal presentation with the decisionmaker at a time when the VM team will have his/her full attention. Be sure that the other stakeholders who will implement the changes are invited and able to attend the presentation. A good idea will never die if it is waiting its turn to be presented. However, it can surely be killed if presented in haste at the wrong time.

Distribute your report (draft or final) in advance to the presentation attendees. In some situations, such as a manufacturing VM study, encourage a wide initial distribution of the report so the stakeholders can read the alternatives and be prepared for the presentation, and, conversely, to ensure that it does not sit on one person's desk waiting for review and a decision about the presentation meeting date. However, in a design/construction VM study, the presentation of results most often occurs on the last day of the workshop. This activity

---

Presentation Outline

1. Identify VM team:
   - Introduce team.
   - Acknowledge other contributors.

2. Identify subject:
   - Outline scope of study.

3. Identify functions studied:
   - Use an abbreviated FAST diagram.
   - Identify basic functions.

4. Provide present cost of functions:
   - Indicate the cost of the item.
   - Relate cost to function.

5. Explain methodology used:
   - Indicate worth of functions.
   - Relate how many ideas were considered.
   - Explain weight evaluation attributes.
   - Relate the performance criteria required.
   - Show selection from top 2 or 3 candidates.

6. Give specific recommendations:
   - Recommend specific changes.

7. Discuss expected benefits:
   - Review life cycle costs.
   - Review break-even analysis.
   - Review return on investment.
   - Explain intangible benefits.

8. Discuss specific implementation plan:
   - Propose a plan to implement.
   - Indicate implementation cost and timing.
   - Indicate consequences of delay.

9. Ask for action:
   - Offer your services.
   - Be prepared to answer questions.

should be scheduled and noted in the workshop agenda so the stakeholders will be prepared for the meeting. The draft VM alternatives are distributed at the presentation of results meeting.

Rehearse your presentation with your team members. The presentation structure may be useful in one or two formats. For instance, the VM facilitator may present the results of the study alone with assistance from the team members as necessary to clarify technical components. A second approach may be for the VM facilitator to act again as the facilitator and have each team member present those alternatives which relate to his/her discipline or area of expertise. The facilitator must decide which way will best present the team's work.

Right before and during the meeting:

- Set up and make sure your visuals are working (best done ten to fifteen minutes before the presentation).

- Introduce the team.

- Be positive. Be concise.

- Distribute the team's report (draft or final) and, as appropriate, ask that the draft implementing instructions be signed and issued.

- Do not read the screen. Know what is on the screen and paraphrase the important points.

> The presentation may be up to two-hours long depending on the project. Typically, spend no more than five minutes to explain one value alternative. If you spark their interest during the presentation, busy people will spend more time with you to ask for more information.

Top management is concerned with net benefit and disposition. Therefore, be sure to address the following points:

- Item/system performance is not adversely affected.
- Supporting technical information is complete and accurate within the time limits of the VM workshop.
- Potential savings are based on valid cost analysis with break-even, ROI, and life cycle cost data.
- The change is feasible.

Remember, sell your ideas! Use your human relations skills. Praise the project team for the work they have done to date. Do not blame anyone or any organizational unit for poor value. Create a positive work environment, and listen to the players in the ensuing discussion to ensure you are effective in conveying the benefits of the change(s) you propose. The boss just spent his/her good money on having your team discover ways to improve value and will get no return on investment for the VM study unless change is implemented. So praise those who will help you approve and implement the idea! In addition, offer your services and those of your team to assist in implementing the recommendations.

The presentation of results should typically be viewed as the time to share information and ensure that the project team understands the changes and benefits of the alternatives put forth. Some alternatives will be obvious winners, and there will be little need to discuss the decision to implement. Others may take a little thought and research. Therefore, a separate meeting should generally be held several days or a week or two after the first to formally determine implementation feasibility. This time lets the project team consider how best to proceed. The owner and project team will then meet to finalize the decisions about each alternative and will either:

- Accept the alternative.
- Accept the alternative with modifications.
- Require further study.
- Reject the alternative for specific, documented reasons.

There will obviously be situations in which immediate decisions must be made during the presentation of results—the schedule is usually the motivator in these cases.

Chapter 8

The Value Methodology Job Plan: Postworkshop Activities

Implementation Phase

Purpose

The purpose of this phase is to implement approved value alternatives.

Questions

Answer these questions about the implementation of ideas:

- Is there an implementation schedule?
- Does the delay in implementation jeopardize the expected ROI?
- Can the value study team assist by drafting the revised specifications or drawings to implement the idea?
- Is the product being changed again by those implementing the recommendation?

Procedures

The participation of the VM team in the implementation phase depends on the project and the team's relationship to the owner's team. For instance, a VA team analyzing a piece of equipment or a plant operation, may comprise members of the owner's company team. It would be fairly straightforward for these team members to switch hats and become part of the implementation team.

In other cases, such as with a design project for an infrastructure project, the VM team may be completely composed of independent professionals without a direct relationship to the owner or the design team outside of the VM study. Therefore, it would be difficult for that team to participate in the implementation process.

Depending on the circumstances:

- Assist in implementing the changes as requested by the project owner.
- Monitor each change as it is being implemented.
- Provide vendor assistance. Identify new suppliers for revised materials and parts, and assist in contracting with them as requested.
- Help users understand the change. Ensure that operating manuals and instructions are revised, and provide user training as appropriate.

Follow-up Phase

Purpose
In the follow-up phase, determine whether the implemented VM alternatives work as promised. Assess whether there are opportunities to improve the VM process for future studies.

Questions
Answer these questions about each change:

- Does the change perform as expected?
- Does it achieve the benefit expected?
- Does the user or customer notice or like the change?

- Would you make the same recommendation again?
- Are there ways in which we can improve the VM study process for future efforts?

Procedures

Speak with the project or product manager to obtain feedback on the whole process so it may be enhanced for the next effort. This may include the following steps:

- Review the use of the product or system.
- In the case of products, purchase the product yourself.
- Interview customers/users to see how they feel about the change(s).
- Make a field trip to see the product, project, process, or service in use.
- Check on maintenance records and warranty service calls.
- Consult with vendors and suppliers for performance characteristics and changes.
- Prepare a report to management indicating how the implemented change is performing.

When you have done this, suggest other improvements as appropriate.

Conclusion

The VM Job Plan is a logical process that promotes objective analysis and creative change. Use it to find better value in your products, processes, projects, and services and to inspire your team and colleagues to improve the value of your work.

Chapter 9

Contractual Aspects of Value Engineering for the U.S. Government

Introduction

When contractors generate technically viable and implementable alternatives to save initial and life cycle costs under a U.S. Federal Government contract, they are able to share the savings with the government. The mechanism to implement this savings is called a Value Engineering Change Proposal (VECP).

VE is addressed in part 48 of the Federal Acquisition Regulations (FAR) 48 CFR 203. Every government contract has a VE clause, which may be mandatory, voluntary, or a combination of the two.

What is a VECP?

A VECP is a change to the federal government contract initiated by the contractor using one of three FAR clauses:

- FAR 52.248-1 for supply and services contracts.
- FAR 52.248-2 for architect/engineer contracts.
- FAR 52.248-3 for construction contracts.

What does it do?

A VECP offers contractors an incentive to share cost savings generated by innovative change to a product, project, or service supplied to the government.

Why use it on government contracts?

VECPs enable the government and the contractor to work together to reduce program cost and improve the performance of the product, project, or service supplied. Without the VECP mechanism, the government may not have access to the process or product improvements during production or construction.

What are the benefits?

A VECP results in an equal or better quality product at a lower total ownership cost for the government; it also results in an increase in profit for the contractor.

The benefits to the government may include:

- Lower total ownership cost.
- Improved performance.
- Application of:
  - New technology.
  - New and possibly more energy efficient equipment models.
  - New or better processes.

The benefits of implementing VECPs are also substantial to the contractor, who:

- Realizes an increase in profit—the original contract profit remains whole with savings calculated on changes only.
- Shares in the savings that provide profit not available under other provisions of the contract.

- Achieves profits above the limitations established on government contracts.

- Establishes a reputation as a cost-conscious supplier.

- Improves communication with the customer.

- May obtain usable technology for other product lines.

- Enhances the retention and growth of corporate technical expertise through advanced technology insertion and through fostering a positive working environment.

Each of these benefits—customer satisfaction, planning stability, good financial performance and cash flow—is directly attributable to the elements of partnering between the government and the contractor.

How is a VECP implemented?

Contractors share in savings by submitting and obtaining government acceptance of a VECP with one of two approaches. The basic clause is a voluntary or incentive program in which the contractor is encouraged to propose VECPs using its own resources. The voluntary clause is required for all contracts for which the value is equal to or greater than $100,000, unless an exemption applies. The clause may be used at a lower rate if the contracting officer determines there is a potential for major savings.

The other clause, Alternate I, is mandatory. It is included in the contract language whenever the contracting officer determines that substantial opportunities exist for VE changes. The government pays for this effort as a separate line item. While the contractor still shares in the savings, it does so at a lower rate than under the voluntary clause.

The contracting officer may require a combination of the voluntary and mandatory efforts by inserting Alternate II into the contract language. This specifies the areas to which the mandatory VE requirement will be applied; the remaining areas are then available for voluntary VECP submissions.

FAR 52.248-1 Supply and Services Contracts

What are the details of a supply and services VECP?

A VECP must reduce cost and make a change to the instant contract—other than quantity of deliverable end items—or to the contract type.

The submission of a VECP is the responsibility of the contractor and is only effective by issuance of a formal modification to the contract. While cost savings are a requirement, a VECP may not impair essential functions or characteristics of an item or system. Submission of VECPs can only be accomplished by the use of the appropriate VE contract clause and any changes made must be technically compatible with contract requirements.

VECPs are the result of continually looking for better, less expensive, and more efficient ways of doing business. A number of considerations can be used to identify VE changes, including whether:

- Technology and the state of the art have changed or if new materials, components, techniques, or processes (which are not specified or allowable under the instant contract) are now available.

- Excessive costs have been uncovered in the current design through cost analysis.

- The specifications have been examined and questioned during performance to determine if they are inappropriate, out of date, or overspecified.

- Additional skills, ideas, and information have become available.

- The user's needs have changed based on redefinition of mission, function, or application of the item.

- Multiple product applications are available for a particular function or requirement.

What does a supply and services VECP contain?

The VE clause requires that contractors provide information on eight topics:

1. **Describe the changes and contrasts of the existing requirements and the proposed change.** Be detailed and clear. This is the primary section reviewed for technical approval. It must show how the change meets the technical and functional requirement. Provide justification if the item's functions or characteristics are being altered by the proposed change. Discuss the advantages and disadvantages of the VECP and the effect the change will have on the end item's performance and on any pertinent objective test data.

2. **Identify all contract requirements that will need revision if the VECP is accepted.** This is essential because any VECP must change the current contract requirements and result in a modification.

3. **Identify the unit or item to which the VECP applies.**

---

4. **Present detailed cost estimates for (a) the affected portion of the existing contract requirement, i.e., what is being taken out (the minuses), and (b) the VECP, i.e., what is being proposed or put in (the pluses).** Detail the contractor's (and subcontractor's) development and implementation costs. These cost data demonstrate savings per unit, savings on the instant contract, and any concurrent or future contract savings.

5. **Estimate the net increase in government cost to implement the VECP, including test and evaluation, operations, maintenance, and logistic support costs.** This estimate does not include the administrative costs to process the VECP. This is where the contractor may suggest ways to minimize such costs.

6. **Estimate the impact to the government of the collateral costs of accepting the VECP, including the agency cost of operations, maintenance, logistic support and/or government-furnished property.** Suggest ways to minimize government costs.

7. **Specify the date by which the VECP must be accepted to achieve the maximum cost reduction and the effect on completion time or delivery schedule if not approved by that date.**

8. **Identify the details of any previous submissions of this VECP, including dates, agencies and contracts involved, and any previous government actions related to this VECP or its previous submissions.**

Why is a VECP rejected?

The government may reject a VECP for several reasons, such as:

- Situations in which the nonrecoverable engineering costs are too great.

- Funds to cover these costs are not available.
- The contractor has failed to properly detail or document the VECP.
- The change may adversely impact other system interfaces.
- There is not enough time to make the change.
- The ROI is not large enough to offset the risk of making the change.

Government involvement when a VECP is being considered is important to ensure buy in. Submit an idea in its early stages of development to request the government's comments and concerns before proceeding to full development. Although the government's initial response is not binding, these communications will help the contractor make the correct business decision on VECP development and submission. Remember, under the basic clause (voluntary), the contractor assumes the risk of the development cost until the VECP has been accepted and the contract modification has been awarded. In contrast, the government pays for the VECP development effort under the mandatory clause (Alternate I).

How are the supply and services savings shared?

When a VECP is accepted, the contractor and the government share in the savings. Various sharing ratios may apply, which depend on the contract type and whether the program is voluntary or mandatory. The sharing ratios range from a government/contractor share of 25/75 to 15/85, depending on the type of contract and whether the savings are for the current contract, concurrent contracts, or future contracts, as illustrated in the figure on page 83.

Sharing Rates Under Government Supply and Services Contracts, Excluding Architect/Engineer and Construction Contracts

FAR 48.104-1 Contract Type	Sharing Arrangement[1]			
	Voluntary		Mandatory	
	Instant Contract Rate	Concurrent and Future Contract Rate	Instant Contract Rate	Concurrent and Future Contract Rate
Fixed-price (other than incentive) type, including award fee	50/50 to 25/75	50/50 to 25/75	75/25	75/25
Incentive type (fixed-price or cost reimbursement) other than award fee	2	50/50	2	75/25
Cost-reimbursement (other than incentive) type	75/25 to 50/50	75/25 to 50/50	85/15	85/15

[1] Read as Government Share/Contractor Share

[2] In incentive-type contracts, the contractor's benefit from the VECP will be realized through the contract's profit or fee adjustment formula.

Acquisition savings may be realized on the instant contract, concurrent contracts, and future contracts. The contractor is entitled to a percentage share (as shown in the previous figure) of any net acquisition savings. Net acquisition savings are realized when the total of acquisition savings exceeds the total of government costs and the contractor's allowable development and implementation costs (CADIC). A VECP often results in the growth of the contractor's and government's allowable development and implementation costs, which must be offset before actual savings occur. This may result in negative instant contract savings (NICS). This occurs when the initial quantities are not sufficient to cover the implementation costs in the instant contract cost or price, based on the acceptance of the VECP. FAR clause 52-248-1, paragraph h, provides that NICS be funded by an increase to the affected contract.

The figure on page 85 illustrates how a VECP can result in NICS. In this case, it is not until the third year of the contract that actual savings occur.

The government and the contractor negotiate the details of the sharing arrangement; the decision as to which rate applies and what the sharing period is are made solely at the discretion of the contracting officer. A VECP is accepted with an authorizing contract modification, but a change may be made to the specifications, as appropriate.

Acquisition savings may affect other ongoing contracts and how the agency will acquire these goods or services in the future, making the contractor eligible for additional savings. A VECP may not provide substantial cost savings on the instant contract. However, collateral savings—reductions in the agency's collateral costs, exclusive of acquisition savings—may be shared if so determined by the head of the contracting activity. Collateral costs are those of operations, maintenance, logistic support, and/or government-furnished property.

Negative Instant Contract Savings Example

	Base Year	Year 2	Year 3	Year 4	Year 5	Totals
Original Cost	$60,000	$60,000	$60,000	$60,000	$60,000	
Net Unit Cost	35,000	35,000	35,000	35,000	35,000	
VECP Savings per Unit	25,000	25,000	25,000	25,000	25,000	
Units to Share	200	500	500	500	300	2,000
Total Savings	**5,000,000**	**12,500,000**	**12,500,000**	**12,500,000**	**7,500,000**	**50,000,000**
Minus Implementation Costs:						
Contractor	(18,000,000)					
Government	(2,000,000)					
Total Implementation Costs	**(20,000,000)**					**(20,000,000)**
Gross Savings	**$(15,000,000)**	**$(2,500,000)**	**$10,000,000**	**$22,500,000**	**$30,000,000**	**$30,000,000**

When a VECP affects more than the current contract, the sharing period begins with the first unit accepted under the VECP and ends with the last unit accepted, or thirty-six to sixty months after the first unit was accepted, whichever the contracting officer determines to be the best approach.

For engineering/development contracts and those with low-rate initial production or early production units, this period is not calculated on a calendar basis, but rather on acceptance of a specific quantity of units to be acquired in the future over a period of thirty-six to sixty consecutive months. These months will be established by the contracting officer and cover the highest planned production period.

For future contract sharing under the voluntary program, the sharing period can extend up to five years for all low-rate initial production contracts. This means that the instant contract must remain open during this same period of time. Payment for future savings can be made as contracts are awarded, as deliveries are made, or by using a lump sum payment based on anticipated quantities.

Alternatively, the contracting officer may determine that a no-cost settlement would be in the government's best interest. In this situation, the contractor would keep all the savings on its instant and concurrent contracts. The government would retain the savings on all other concurrent contracts placed with other sources, all future contract savings, and all collateral savings.

> To maximize savings, prepare a VECP as early in the acquisition cycle as possible. If not prepared early, the contractor may not realize any savings for the instant contract (NICS).

> However, future contract savings may still
> make preparation of the VECP worthwhile.

How does VE affect supply and services subcontractors?

The FAR clause provides for the mandatory flow-down of the VE clause in any subcontract greater than $100,000. The provisions may be included in contracts for less than that amount if the contractor determines that there appear to be VE opportunities. The CADIC will include the subcontractor's costs; the contractor may agree to any sharing arrangement it desires with its subcontractor as long as it does not reduce the government's share of savings.

FAR 52.248-2 Architect/Engineer (A/E) Contracts

What is it?

This VE clause is inserted into an A/E's contract when the contracting officer determines that VE application is required.

What does it do?

The clause requires that the A/E perform a VE study of the design documents immediately following completion of the 35% design or at such stages as the contracting officer may direct. Each separately priced line item for VE services should specifically define the scope of work to be accomplished and may include VE studies of items other than design documents. The contractor should be paid as the contract specifies for this effort but should not share in savings that may result from acceptance and use of VE Proposals (VEPs) by the government.

Why use it?

VE workshops performed under the A/E contract during design allow the agency to:

- Identify unnecessary costs in a design.

- Offer alternatives while assuring that quality, reliability, life cycle costs, and other critical factors meet or exceed the customer's expectations.

- Keep VE savings in-house rather than sharing the savings with the construction contractor through the VECP process.

The government will define the scope of the VE study and may specify:

- The number and timing of the studies that will be performed on the project or program, e.g., two VE studies at the 25% and 75% design completion phases.

- The qualifications of the VE team leader (certified value specialist).

- The team member disciplines and registrations/certifications.

- The team composition, e.g., a completely independent team, a team comprising the design team, a team of government professionals.

- The number, format, and distribution of VE study reports, e.g., hard copies, CD-ROM, electronic submission on an ftp site.

How do I do it?

The scope of work will detail specific tasks and submissions for the VE effort. The architect or engineer submits a proposal to the contracting officer for approval, typically comprising a breakdown of labor hours and costs, a project approach, the schedule for completion, and the

---

proposed team structure. Upon approval and receipt of a notice to proceed, the VE study is performed.

What are the requirements for each VEP developed?

The VE team members follow the VM Job Plan defined in this pocket guide and include the following information in each VEP:

- A description of the difference between the existing and proposed design, the comparative advantages and disadvantages of each, a justification when an item's function is being altered, the effect of the change on system or facility performance, and any pertinent objective test data.

- A list and analysis of design criteria or specifications that must be changed if the VEP is accepted.

- A separate detailed estimate of the impact on project cost of each VEP if accepted and implemented by the government.

- A description and estimate of costs that the government may incur in implementing the VEP, such as design change costs and test and evaluation costs.

- A prediction of any effects that the proposed change may have on life cycle cost.

- The effect the VEP will have on design or construction schedules.

What happens after the VE study effort?

Following the VE workshop, the government reviews the VEPs that were developed and determines implementation. Approved VEPs are implemented by bilateral modification to the A/E contract. Costs to implement the VEP into the design are paid by the government. The A/E contractor does not receive a share of any cost avoidance or savings as a result of the implemented VEPs.

FAR 52.248-3 Construction Contracts

Contractors are encouraged to develop, prepare, and submit VECPs in a process similar to that of supply and acquisition VECPs, **except:**

- VECPs on construction contracts are not mandatory per the FAR.

- A contractor may share in instant contract and collateral savings realized from an accepted VECP, unless the contracting officer has included FAR 52.248-3 Alternate I to disallow collateral savings sharing arrangements.

- This construction clause does not allow for sharing of savings on future or concurrent contracts.

- The contractor must submit any VECP to the resident engineer at the work site with a copy to the contracting officer. Copies should also be furnished to the VE officer.

- The contractor should include an appropriate VE clause in any construction subcontract of $50,000 or more and may include one in subcontracts of lesser value. The contractor may choose any arrangement for subcontractor VE incentive payments since these payments do not affect the government's share of the savings resulting from the VECP.

- A VECP submitted under this construction clause must include seven of the eight items noted earlier for the supply and services clause. The "identification of the unit to which the VECP applies" is normally not identifiable in construction.

The government contracting officer will notify the contractor of the status of the VECP within forty-five calendar days after its receipt. Status may mean making an appointment to discuss, negotiating, providing a justification for rejection, or providing a reason why additional time is required by the government to consider the VECP and stating the expected date of the decision. The government is not liable for delay in acting upon a VECP. The contractor is bound by the existing contract until a notice to proceed or a modification is issued.

A VECP may be accepted in whole or in part by the contracting officer's award of a modification to the contract. The VECP may be accepted, even though an agreement on price reduction has not been reached, simply by issuing a notice to proceed. If the VECP is not accepted, the contracting officer will notify the contractor in writing, explaining the reasons for rejection. The decision to accept or reject all or part of any VECP is a unilateral decision made solely at the discretion of the contracting officer.

How are construction savings calculated and shared?

The government's share of savings is determined by subtracting government costs from instant contract savings and multiplying the result by:

- 45% for fixed-price contracts.
- 75% for cost-reimbursement contracts.

The following is an example of a fixed-price contract VECP computation.

Initial contract price:

Materials	$5,400,000
Labor	6,000,000
Profit	600,000
Total	$12,000,000

A contractor's VECP notes that market prices are significantly lower on a material comparable to that specified. The comparable material offers the same quality as that specified in the contract and is much easier to construct, meaning that schedule can be shortened as well. The contractor's proposal includes the following costs.

New materials	$ 4,000,000
Labor	5,000,000
Contractor's cost to develop, test, prepare, and submit VECP	10,000
Subcontractor's cost to develop, test, prepare, submit VECP	150,000
Total	$ 9,160,000

The government questions quality, so an additional $70,000 is expended on government tests to ensure acceptability. (Normal administrative costs to process the VECP do not enter into calculations.)

The estimated reduction in contractor cost of performing
$11,400,000 - $9,000,000 = $ 2,400,000

Contractor development and implementation costs
$10,000 + $150,000 =   160,000

Instant contract savings
$2,400,000 - $160,000 =   2,240,000

Government share of instant contract savings
($2,240,000 - $70,000) x 0.45 =   976,500

Contractor's share of instant contract savings
($2,240,000 - $70,000) x 0.55 =   1,193,500

After acceptance, the new contract price is:

The original contract price	12,000,000
minus the instant contract savings	(2,240,000)
Plus the contractor's savings share	1,193,500
Equals the new contract price	$ 10,953,500

This is an increase in contractor profit from $600,000 to $1,793,500 while saving the government $976,500.

Where collateral savings are allowed, the instant contract amount will be increased by 20% of any projected collateral savings to be realized in a typical year of use after subtracting any government costs not previously offset. However, the contractor's share of collateral savings cannot exceed the contract's firm-fixed price or estimated cost at the time the VECP is accepted, or $100,000, whichever is greater. The contracting officer is the sole determiner of the amount of collateral savings.

The contractor may include the following statement on affected parts to restrict the government's right to use any part of a VECP or the supporting data prior to VECP acceptance:

> These data, furnished under the Value Engineering–Construction clause of contract "X", shall not be disclosed outside the Government or duplicated, used, or disclosed, in whole or in part, for any purpose other than to evaluate a value engineering change proposal submitted under the clause. This restriction does not limit the Government's right to use information contained in these data if it has been obtained or is otherwise available from the Contractor or from another source without limitations.

If a VECP is accepted, the contractor grants the government unlimited rights in the remaining portions of the VECP and supporting data.

A contractor should review the contract for VE clauses to ascertain the avenue to proffer cost-saving proposals. If there is no VE clause in the contract and the contractor has a proposal that has merit, a contract modification should be requested to include the appropriate VE clause, and then the proposal(s) should be submitted.

Conclusion

Voluntary VECP development and submission should be viewed as a potentially profitable investment by the contractor. The contractor should apply the appropriate business analysis decision processes when deciding to proceed with VECP development and submission. Advance communication with the government and complete detailed VECP submissions help to minimize the processing time of VECPs. The government is required to give the contractor a status of the VECP review within forty-five days of submission. A contract modification and a cost reduction must result from an approved VECP.

Appendix A

Function Analysis Systems Technique

What is FAST?

Function Analysis Systems Technique (FAST) is a powerful analytical tool developed in 1964 by Charles W. Bytheway, who published this innovation at a SAVE conference in 1965. This contribution to the VM tool kit added a new dimension to the VM Job Plan that set VM apart from other analytical techniques.

Function, in the case of VM, is described as an active verb and a measurable noun. Function-based descriptions establish a common language for the facilitator and the team. Once functions are defined by this verb/noun method, teams determine what function is basic to the item of study. Basic is defined as the function the item must perform. Without it, the product, service, system, or organization cannot provide the intended use for the customer. For example, a ballpoint pen cannot deliver the function of "make mark" or "communicate information" without performing the function of "dispense fluid."

How does it work?

Once functions are determined, the team constructs a precedent logic-based orientation of functions by asking the question "How?" and moving from the basic function toward the right. Once all the functions are oriented in the "How?" logic dimension, that logic is tested by moving toward the left and asking the question "Why?" Each function has a precedent dependency moving in both directions, from left to right and right to left.

The far left side of the linear diagram contains what are called higher order output functions. The far right is referred to as lower order input functions. A scope line is normally drawn to delineate the lowest order input function from the function that represents the scope of study. Similarly, the highest order output functions are delineated by a scope line between them and the basic function. The figure on page 97 offers examples of diagrams and conventions.

Secondary functions support the basic function. In many instances, secondary functions may not be required or can be altered so that the function supporting the basic function is retained for a lower total cost of effective ownership. In some instances, duplicate functions are identified as well as functions not being performed, which, if performed, would increase the value of the function and ultimately of the product to the end user.

Other dimensions of the diagram include a "When?" function, which is oriented below critical path functions to describe other secondary functions that support basic or secondary functions. Functions aligned across a FAST model horizontally on the x-axis form what is typically referred to as a critical path. Objective or specification functions can be oriented in two ways. The first is a typical convention where the function is indicated above the basic function. The alternate method is to make a separate box of objective or specification functions that the product, service, system, or organization is expected to satisfy. Independent supporting functions may also be represented and may form a secondary minor critical path.

Other types of functions are:

- **All time functions** are functions that can apply anywhere in the process. For example, "Assure safety" is a function that can apply anywhere in the model or diagram.

Ground Rules: Function Analysis Systems Technique (FAST) Model

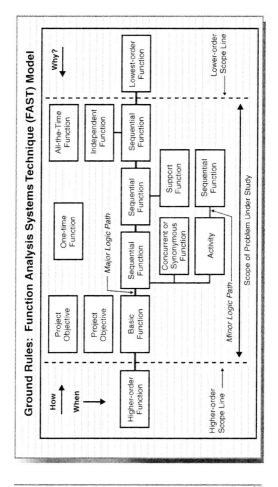

- **Point in time functions** are functions that recur at particular points in the diagram.
- **Design objective functions** are used with classical FAST diagrams to indicate design, business goal, or specification functions.

Conventions

1. **Logic gates between functions that move along the critical path left to right or right to left are:**

    - And gate.

    - And/or gate.

    - Conditional or gate.

2. **Logic gates traverse the diagram when moving left to right or right to left.**

Function diagrams and models allow the practitioner and teams to have a visual representation of the product, services, system, or organization in a precedent logic format. As such, the team can analyze whether there are opportunities to improve in order to maintain the performance of a function without degrading quality, maintainability, reliability, or safety criteria.

The next component of the function diagramming and modeling process allows the team and practitioner to add other dimensional characteristics to function, such as cost in the form of labor, time, and materials, to produce a resulting function contribution. Using the function orientation to represent costs is another powerful feature of this technique. When cost is represented by function, it reveals a true cost perspective of what it takes to perform or produce a contribution of a function. When costs are represented by function, the team can analyze the cost, worth, and value of the function; determine which 20% of functions contain 80% of costs; establish targets for brainstorming improvement; and determine opportunities to combine, reduce, streamline, or eliminate undesired functions.

Procedures

1. **Identify functions.** List individual functions on Post-it Notes® (stickies), and mount a large piece of flip chart paper or butcher paper on a large wall.

2. **Orient stickies by function type on separate individual flip chart sheets.**

3. **Determine the basic function and place on the wall-mounted paper.**

4. **Ask how the basic function is achieved or performed.** The resulting function statement is placed to the right of the basic function.

5. **Check the logic of these function relationships by asking why this added function is achieved or performed, moving left, back toward the basic function.** The answer should be the achievement or performance of the basic function.

6. **If, after asking the how or why questions, the answer does not logically fit, there is a logic mismatch that must be resolved.**

When do I use FAST?

FAST is typically used during the function analysis phase of the VM/VE Job Plan. However, it can be used during the preworkshop activity as a method to validate scope, identify problems, and generate preliminary opportunities for improvement. In other instances, FAST modeling and diagramming can be used as a stand-alone tool or with teams to help gain a functional understanding of functions and function relationships.

Ultimately, FAST models and diagrams become a tool for effective communication of products, services, processes, and organizations.

Appendix B

Delphi

Introduction

Delphi is both a tool for creativity and a method of achieving consensus by identifying design options and speculating on their outcome. Delphi involves individual contributions of information, assessment of the group judgment, an opportunity for individuals to debate and revise their views, and a degree of anonymity. Because individual responses in a Delphi session are recorded on paper or electronically and submitted anonymously, the technique is especially useful in overcoming the emotional blocks often encountered in brainstorming. A Delphi group would normally include all stakeholders associated with the item being studied, including the owner, designer, constructor/manufacturer, manager, and value engineer.

A major advantage of Delphi is that it minimizes the bias of personality in achieving a group opinion. This method may be used for:

- Exploring design options.
- Identifying the pros and cons of potential options.
- Developing an understanding of complex projects.
- Exposing the priorities of personal values and design goals.

Any group discussion is likely to produce a majority position, but it is often a compromise rather than a true consensus. This compromise may reflect the opinion of the most verbal, most dynamic, or most persistent group members. In the early stage of design, where a significant degree of uncertainty prevails, it is imprudent to assume that any one person's opinion is more valid than another's. It is important to understand the range of opinions within the group and the reasons for individual estimates. It is immaterial whether Delphi participants are involved in the design under consideration, as long as each person provides a reasonable estimate based on knowledge of various design alternatives. Once assimilated, these estimates provide valuable information in their differences as well as in their similarities.

Design Options

The logic of the Delphi methodology is such that the team will gradually converge on a set of design alternatives judged by consensus to provide optimum performance for the problem in question. As shown in the figure on page 103, the Delphi process goes through a number of individual and group exploration cycles and concludes with a group recommendation. The first Delphi cycle provides an a priori set of inputs, which are subjective in nature, about a desired system. On the basis of these inputs, the team compiles a set of design alternatives. Estimated cost targets are then reviewed—without revealing their authorship—in order to determine the range of target values. The group can then begin to order the desired system properties into logical and probable design options, each of which is associated with an index of desirability known only to each participant.

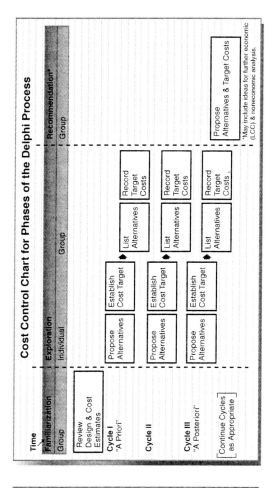

Cost Control Chart for Phases of the Delphi Process

Time	Familiarization	Exploration		Recommendation*
	Group	Individual	Group	Group
	Review Design & Cost Estimates			
Cycle I "A Priori"		Propose Alternatives → Establish Cost Target	List Alternatives → Record Target Costs	
Cycle II		Propose Alternatives → Establish Cost Target	List Alternatives → Record Target Costs	
Cycle III "A Posteriori"		Propose Alternatives → Establish Cost Target	List Alternatives → Record Target Costs	Propose Alternatives & Target Costs
[Continue Cycles as Appropriate]				

*May include ideas for further economic (LCC) & noneconomic analysis.

©2008 GOAL/QPC

The second cycle of the Delphi process allows each participant individually to digest the group ranking and focus on the most desirable design options. Participants can add or modify design options at this stage; meanwhile, empirical confirmation of the range of target cost values further reinforces the validity of previous choices. As a part of the search, Delphi may predict the obsolescence of certain technology. It is then possible to take corrective action by adding features, such as new, innovative technology.

Once participants have completed the second cycle of Delphi, the group reassembles. Individual responses are fed into a formal group discussion in order to integrate a priori and a posteriori data. If the design options remain virtually unchanged, with an indication of which alternatives are more desirable, the group is ready to make recommendations. Usually, however, at least one additional cycle is required before consensus is reached, although target cost values for the system should continue to converge.

The graphs shown on page 105 illustrate the degree of each participant's confidence in his/her target estimate for various design courses of action. The a priori (before consensus) estimate greatly improves with the number of Delphi cycles. As the cycles converge on a group consensus (a posteriori), so do the design courses of action. In this manner, design cost control is exercised.

The final step of Delphi involves group participation in proposing alternatives and target costs for the system(s) under study. Design options recommended at this stage may still require further economic (e.g., life cycle cost) and noneconomic review as details of specific components are identified.

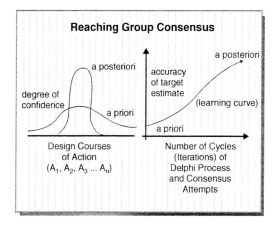

Reaching Group Consensus

degree of confidence

a posteriori

a priori

Design Courses
of Action
$(A_1, A_2, A_3 \ldots A_n)$

accuracy
of target
estimate

a posteriori

(learning curve)

a priori

Number of Cycles
(Iterations) of
Delphi Process
and Consensus
Attempts

A Delphi Case Study

A worksheet (see page 106) can be used to aid decision-making during each cycle of the Delphi process. The form is organized to document all pertinent information submitted by each individual during every cycle of the Delphi process. The building component or system being studied is described in the block in the upper left. The estimated cost of that element may be entered and a system component breakdown with related costs may be listed on the lines below the block. Functions to be performed by the element may be entered as conventional function analysis, or verb/noun, descriptions.

Delphi Technique Applied to Exterior Closure

VALUE OPPORTUNITIES
The Delphi Method

Project: Office Building
Location: Downtown, USA
Date:

Cycle: 1
Sheet: 4
Phase: Concept

Exterior Closure Brick & Block Composite Wall	Item Description	Ideas

Target Cost	$32.00/WSF
Estimated Cost	$41.33/WSF

Functions (verb-noun)

Enclose	Space
Control	Noise
Enhance	Aesthetics
Insulate	Space

Components	Cost per SF of Wall Labor	Material
Face brick veneer	$ 6.11	$15.44
Wash brick	$ 0.53	$ 1.32
Concrete block backup	$ 2.46	$ 8.51
Wall ties	$ 0.08	$ 0.21
Perlite insulation	$ 0.59	$ 0.44
Flashing, aluminum	$ 0.17	$ 0.59
Shelf angle	$ 1.07	$ 1.37
Control joint	$ 0.21	$ 0.08
Backer rod & sealant	$ 0.04	$ 0.57
Collar joint	$ 0.69	$ 0.86
Total	$11.95	$29.39
Labor & material		$41.33

Ideas

Cast-in-place concrete
Precast concrete
Tilt-up concrete
Concrete block wall
Split-face block wall
Solid brick wall
Stone veneer with stud backup
Stone veneer with block backup
Brick veneer with stud backup
Brick veneer block backup
Aluminum metal siding panel with backup
Painted metal siding panel with backup
Plywood finish with wood stud backup
Metal finish with wood stud backup
Stucco finish with wood stud backup
Glass curtain wall
Tile finish on block walls
Tile finish on concrete walls

Rationale/Assumptions

Maintain insulation value of R-19
Area of wall is 70,000 SF
Location is in cold, dry climate

As each participant begins to understand the design through function analysis, alternatives will come to mind. Space is provided on the right side of the sheet to record design ideas. After adequate consideration of alternative courses of action, each participant estimates a minimum target cost necessary to perform the required functions. The rationale and assumptions underlying the target cost are noted at the bottom of the sheet. Upon completion of the Delphi consensus process, this target figure becomes the cost objective for the element under study.

Applying this format to the design of an office facility and following the Delphi method, a multidisciplinary team consisting of a group leader, a client representative, the architect, a structural engineer, and a mechanical engineer reviews the exterior closure requirements for the project. A list of functions that the exterior closure of the building is expected to satisfy is provided to the team along with an estimate of costs. After design requirements are reviewed, each participant is asked to list ideas for satisfying the functions of the exterior closure. The worksheet illustrates how one individual completes the Delphi sheet during the first cycle.

After each participant has completed the worksheet, including a targeted cost for the exterior closure, the team is assembled. All ideas are then listed on a flip chart for group discussion. In all, forty-four different ideas are listed in this example. Ideas range from wood construction to more elaborate masonry construction. As group discussion begins to organize random ideas into packages, certain ideas are judged as having significantly more potential than others. Additional study teams are invited to participate in the discussion.

The second cycle of the Delphi process begins with individual team members excluding some ideas from further consideration and developing new alternatives. A list of alternatives that meet functional criteria is discussed by team members. The client is also given an opportunity to comment on proposed alternatives.

By the third and final iteration, various team members begin to agree on key points. The structural engineer proposes using load bearing masonry walls in lieu of brick veneer walls. The mechanical engineer recommends use of heavier insulation, such as polystyrene insulation, in lieu of perlite insulation. The architect suggests an articulated decorative brick pattern to enhance the aesthetics of the office building.

The Delphi process is repeated until a satisfactory consensus is reached. However, at times not all participants might agree on a single outcome. Some opinions may be based on significantly different rationales, each of which is so cogent to the individual(s) proposing them that consensus is impossible. This situation may lead to a more thorough follow-up analysis and revisions of the design problem.

Appendix C

Target Costing

Target costing is a powerful concept that is an integral part of a coordinated, companywide cost management process, which in turn is a major component of a holistic, companywide strategic management process. In short, target costing is an essential part of a unified approach to companywide profit planning.

Target costing is a proactive way to ensure that a desired profit is achieved in a project. This integrated, company-wide approach is aimed at ensuring that each of the company's endeavors is profitable at planned levels. Target costing treats costs as an input to the product development process.

The target costing process steps are not extraordinary; however, the results of consistently following them are. In the early 1960s, Toyota developed a cost management process now commonly called *genka kaikaku*, or target costing, and transformed itself from a nearly bankrupt company to the most profitable company in Japan. The results of target costing include:

- Bringing the product to market faster.
- Improving design efficiency.
- Lowering development cost.
- Reducing product cost.
- Developing components that can be manufactured more easily.

- Developing products that are easier to assemble.
- Simplifying processes.
- Improving technology.
- Integrating superior quality.

Toyota's target costing system emulated the design-to-cost methodology developed in the United States. However, in the early 1970s during the rollout of a Corolla that met all of its cost targets, Toyota realized that the auto did not meet its expected profitability targets. This caused a major shift in Toyota's thinking and target costing philosophy. The result was an enhancement of the design-to-cost system to something more like a design-to-profit system. Now research shows that most Japanese definitions of *genka kaikaku* depict target costing as a profit management technique.

Target costing is based on the formula of market price minus profit equals target cost. Since global competition has intensified over the last decade, the consumer has a growing influence on the price he/she will pay for goods and services. Thus, corporations have little control over the selling price of their products. Since this is a design-to-profit system, the corporation needs to focus as an aggregate on the profitability of the enterprise. When the target profit is subtracted from the target selling price, the result is the target cost.

Target costing without VM does not work well. Conversely, in product development, VM works best when used in a target costing environment, especially in the earliest stage of the product development process. The most experienced companies apply VM prior to the concept development phase. (See the figure on page 111.)

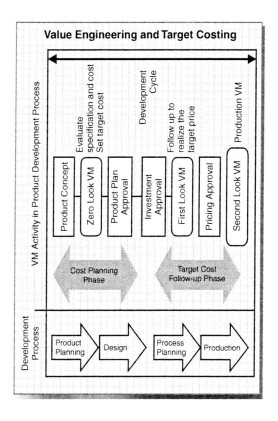

Value Engineering and Target Costing

Companies face challenges to successfully implement target costing. The first is the need for a change in leadership attitudes and performance metrics. Performance metrics for corporate leaders do not traditionally encourage the environment necessary for target costing to flourish.

Another challenge relates to the recognition of cost avoidances by the company. The best money to save is money never spent. Most corporations have significant objectives across all business sectors for cost savings but nothing for cost avoidance. Thus, because target costing is all about cost avoidance, these stated objectives discourage its use.

The third major impediment to implementation is knowledge of and ability to recall conversion costs. Most large Japanese corporations have been collecting detailed conversion costs related to part numbers in areas that most Western companies treat as overhead or burden. When these costs are not related to a part number, they must be allocated across all part numbers within a cost group. When this type of allocation occurs, accurate cost estimating is not possible.

Cost tables are developed to place costs into a format that is easy for design engineers to use. Since design engineers create cost, they need to know what cost they are creating from the beginning. Once the cost tables have been established for some time, they can be converted into cost algorithms, which can then be integrated into CAD workstations. As designs develop on the computer with shapes, features, dimensions, tolerances, surface finishes, material selection, and volume information, estimated costs are immediately given to the designer.

Organization structure is another change that needs to occur for target costing to thrive. Companies like Toyota, Sharp, Canon, Nissan, Isuzu, and numerous others have up to 200 people assigned to a cost planning group. Each cost planning group is responsible for the following functions:

- The analysis of market price, value, and volume.
- The establishment of a target profit for a new product.

- The establishment of a target cost and allocation of the target.

- The review of initial cost estimates, including all variable, fixed, and investment costs.

- The development of an action plan to achieve the established targets.

- The responsibility of implementing the action plan.

- The maintenance of cost status throughout the life of product.

- The use of VM.

- The development of new cost improving methodologies.

Applying this process properly will most certainly require a company to rethink its entire strategic planning process and its costing philosophy. Despite the difficulty of change, the payoff is high. Over four decades of Japanese experience stand as a testimony to the power of target costing to deliver planned profit and, in so doing, to keep the organization constantly focused on delivering value. Western companies that can adopt target costing the soonest and fastest will find that they have a very important strategic and competitive edge that will take them far in the future.

Appendix D

Voice of the Customer and Quality Function Deployment

Voice of the Customer

It is essential to understand the qualitative and quantitative wants of the customer in order to provide the highest value to him/her. One of the first steps in assessing the voice of the customer is to determine who the customer is. Customers may include the following:

- A dealer, distributor, or retailer.
- A governmental organization.
- An installer.
- Leasing and rental companies.
- Maintenance personnel.
- Original equipment manufacturer (OEM) customers.
- An operator or end user.
- An owner.
- A purchaser.

Customers from various market segments should be represented when obtaining the voice of the customer. Market segments may include consumers and commercial, industrial, governmental, military, and international organizations.

There are a number of ways to obtain the voice of the customer. Some of the methods include:

- Interviews (face-to-face and phone).
- Surveys (mail, phone, and internet).
- Observations at the location of usage.
- Customer feedback.
- Focus groups.
- Trade shows.
- Customer panels and councils.
- Service calls.

Personnel involved in conducting interviews and designing surveys must be trained. Market research firms can be consulted to help with the voice-of-the-customer activities. Typical market surveys do not have the necessary detail on the value perceived by the customer for various functions. Therefore, it is best if members of the VM team participate in determining the voice of the customer. The VM team members can help to ensure that adequate cost information is obtained during the voice-of-the-customer research. The resulting information can be used when developing target costs.

It is necessary to determine how important each function is to the customer. The common value measurement techniques include the following:

- Simple ranking in which functions are ranked in order of importance.

- Pair comparison in which the functions to be judged are presented in all possible pairs. A scale is then created as each item is weighed against every other item. Finally, the functions are listed and ranked in order of merit.

- Direct Magnitude Estimation (DME) in which participants assign numerical indicators to the list of items as a function of relative merit. The ratings from the participants are averaged and normalized.

- Nested Hierarchy Process (NHP), a tree-like hierarchy in which the number of levels of features varies from two to four is typically used. It is important to have features and functions at the same level of indenture for analysis.

- Scoring models in which a performance measurement scale is established for each criterion. Alternatives are scored against the established performance measurement scale.

- Value graphs in which the importance score is plotted against the satisfaction score. Items that have high importance and low satisfaction need to be addressed.

- Utility curves in which the metric is plotted against the degree of fulfillment. The curve shapes may be linear, logarithmic, s-curves, step functions, and so on. The curves help visualize the effect of diminishing returns.

- Conjoint analysis, a tool which allows the use of a subset of the possible combinations of product features in determining the relative importance of each feature in the purchasing decision. Conjoint analysis is also called a multi-attribute compositional model. The data is processed by statistical software using Hierarchical Bayesian and other procedures.

Quality Function Deployment (QFD)

QFD is a tool that takes the voice-of-the-customer data and presents it in a matrix format. Yoji Akao introduced the concept of QFD in Japan in 1966. It was used at the Kobe shipyards of Mitsubishi Heavy Industries in 1972, and integrated with VE in the early 1980s.

QFD has five major steps:

1. Understand the customer.

2. Gather the voice of the customer.

3. Develop the matrix to translate the customer's input into the design team's performance objectives.

4. Develop matrices to select concepts and identify specifications.

5. Develop a matrix to link product specifications to manufacturing conditions.

QFD analysis can contain up to thirty matrices. The first matrix is referred to as the house of quality and is the most important. It is depicted in the figure below.

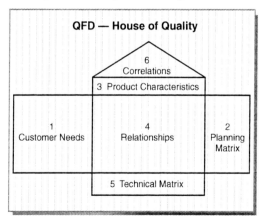

Room 1—Customer needs. Customer needs are also sometimes referred to as customer benefits, customer requirements, demanded quality, voices, wants, and what.

The customer needs include an importance rating by the customer with a rating scale of one to five.

Room 2—Planning matrix. Room 2 contains data from customers on the perceived value of our product and the competitor products. It includes the following items:

- Quantitative market data.
- The customer's competitive assessment.
- Customer satisfaction with current product.
- Customer satisfaction with competitors.
- The goal setting for new product.
- The rank ordering the customer wants.

Room 3—Product characteristics. Room 3 describes how to meet the customer needs. The product characteristics are also sometimes referred to as corporate expectations, design requirements, how, process requirements, product requirements, quality characteristics, technical performance measures, technical requirements, and technical response.

Room 4—Relationships. Room 4 contains a matrix that quantifies the strength of the relationship between each element of the customer needs and the product characteristics. Symbols with numerical values are used to indicate a strong, medium, or weak relationship.

Room 5—Technical matrix. The technical matrix contains the following items:

- Technical performance targets.
- Information on the competitor's performance from published literature, tests, and tear-down analysis.
- The rank ordering of technical responses based on customer wants.

- Additional information, such as specifications, difficulty, risk assessment, and any special requirements.

Room 6—Correlations. The roof of the house contains the assessments of the interrelationships between the elements of the product characteristics. Symbols are used to indicate strong positive, positive, negative, or strong negative correlations.

Appendix E

Lean Enterprise Value

For detailed information about lean manufacturing, please reference *The Lean Enterprise Memory Jogger™*.

The objective of this appendix is to describe how to best integrate VM and lean manufacturing. VM was a predominant technique long before the concept of lean manufacturing became popular. Based on the Toyota production system, lean manufacturing focuses on adding stakeholder value. It does not necessarily focus on the functions of processes, which is the main feature of VM. So, the combination of these methodologies creates increased power and substantially improves results. For the purpose of this guide, we will call the combination of these two practices Lean Enterprise Value (LEV).

LEV is most commonly used on processes. These processes can be in the manufacturing facility or in the office environment. Essentially any process can be improved using LEV. Administrative functions in an office environment, health care, banks, and law enforcement systems are just a few of the countless areas to apply LEV.

In manufacturing, in addition to identifying and eliminating waste, the use of the VM Job Plan forces the team to analyze the function of each step of the process. As you now know, a function is a two-word combination of an active verb and a measurable noun.

A novice to VM may say that "Stamp part" or "Drill hole" are functions. In fact, these do not fit the function definition, since they lack the abstraction necessary to become functions. If we were to brainstorm "Drill hole," our thoughts and ideas would be extremely limited to drilling a hole. By taking a more abstract approach, such as "Create orifice" or "Make opening," a team can brainstorm many new ways to perform this function. The human mind thus becomes unconstrained and will not think only of drilling a hole. Similarly, the function of stamping a part could be "Form shape." One can imagine many new thoughts of forming a shape as opposed to stamping a part. What good is it to eliminate all the waste out of a stamped part process when a forging, injection molding, or other process is better and more cost effective? LEV gives the user the opportunity to decide the best process to perform the function and also to eliminate the waste in that best process.

In all situations, LEV activities follow the VM Job Plan. However, the information phase is enhanced to include team member understanding of lean and synchronous concepts, to study and analyze the process under study with this knowledge, and to find and record all types of waste for the particular process being studied. Value stream mapping or sequence flow charts can be used to document all the steps of the process being studied. For each step, the actual time to perform the step needs to be recorded. To fully understand the lead time, the elapsed time for each step also needs to be recorded. For example, the actual time to move a tub of parts to an operator station may be .003 minutes per part, but since the parts may sit there waiting to be used for more than eight hours, the lapsed time could be 480 minutes. An office example is a supervisor who reviews and approves an expense report in about ten minutes, although the report may sit on the supervisor's desk for a day before and after the signature step occurs. Thus, the elapsed time would be 1440 minutes. Every step of the process needs to have this data.

In the function analysis phase of the VM Job Plan, the functions of each step of the process are developed. The figure below shows a list of process steps and their appropriate functions.

Manufacturing Process

Piston Rack Operations	Verb	Noun
Blank part	Form	Shape
Wash part	Remove	Contamination
Grind	Smooth	Surface
Broach and deburr	Form	Attachment
	Smooth	Edges
Mill and deburr	Form	Interface
	Smooth	Edges
Wash	Remove	Contamination
Straighten	Maintain	Shape
	Maintain	Tolerances
Drill and deburr	Create	Orifice
	Smooth	Edges
Broach Hole	Create	Orifice
Finish Grind	Smooth	Surface
Cut Length	Establish	Length
	Maintain	Tolerances
Deburr	Smooth	Edges
	Remove	Material
Remove Dust	Remove	Contamination
Others	Maintain	Inventory
	Transport	Material
	Receive	Material

The continuance of the function analysis phase would lead to developing a FAST Diagram. In the figure on page 123, that random list of functions is used to create a FAST Diagram.

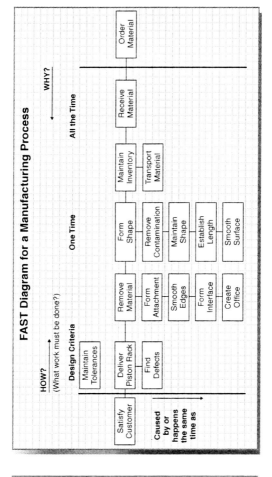

FAST Diagram for a Manufacturing Process

HOW?
(What work must be done?)

WHY?

Design Criteria | One Time | All the Time

Maintain Tolerances

Satisfy Customer — Deliver Piston Rack — Remove Material — Form Shape — Maintain Inventory — Receive Material — Order Material

Find Defects

Form Attachment / Remove Contamination

Smooth Edges / Maintain Shape

Form Interface / Establish Length

Create Office / Smooth Surface

Transport Material

Caused by or happens the same time as

The next step would be to create a time-to-function relationship matrix that would assist the team to decide which functions offer the greatest opportunity for value improvement.

An example of LEV outside of manufacturing is in the product development process of a large automotive company. In this case, the term lean engineering was used to make the process special to the engineering organization that was using LEV. In most industries today, fast-to-market is essential to win against the competition. The product development cycle thus becomes the critical, key link to an organization's success. The faster a company can develop and implement a new design, the better its chance of becoming first to market with a key new technology, appearance, or clever product scheme. Companies must now excel by moving design concepts from the drawing board—though actual drawing boards are a thing of the past, with all new designs on the computer using 3-D software and math models—to the production floor and into the showroom.

Quality designs have been a given for many years. To ensure company profitability, cost competitive designs have been given high consideration for many years as well. But now, rapid product development time is getting the same consideration. In addition to completing designs in record time, the cost to produce designs is extremely critical. Engineering resources are at a premium. Thus, it behooves an organization to make the design community as effective and efficient as possible. This is what we call the lean engineering factory. The same process described above for a manufacturing facility is applied to a very complex product development process. The first step is to detail the process that is to be studied, as in manufacturing. Next, the team needs to identify the waste in the process. Some practitioners refine their lean engineering presentation materials so that designers and engineers can relate to the concepts. Then, as stated above, the team

FAST Diagram for a Major Phase in Product Development Processes

HOW? → ← WHY?

	Design Objectives	One-time Functions	All the Time Functions	
HIGHER ORDER FUNCTIONS	Accomplish Specifications	Establish Tolerances	Conduct Reviews	
	Meet Regulations		Obtain Approvals	
Issue Product/ Process	Release Math	Create Geometry	Receive Requirements	Develop Requirements
	Submit Data (Databank)	Conduct Analysis	Understand Requirements	
	Transmit Data (Purch/supp.)	Confirm Interfaces	Apply Strategy (GD & T)	
		Develop Transitional Surfaces		
		Create Surfaces		
		Finalize Surfaces		
		Validate Clearance		
		Construct Properties		

again moves to the function analysis phase, including the development of a FAST Diagram. The figure on page 125 depicts a FAST Diagram for the designer's effort to create 3-D math models.

Following and utilizing the remainder of the VM Job Plan will yield results that cannot be achieved via other methods.

Appendix F

Design for Manufacture and Assembly

Introduction

Design for Manufacture and Assembly (DFMA) is a very powerful technique within the VM toolbox when applied to manufactured products and processes in the industrial community. DFMA is most effective when applied early in a product's or process's design cycle. Its main purpose is to determine the most cost-effective, optimized design for any given product or process when manufacturing is considered. DFMA not only evaluates the various components, selected materials, and process assembly order, but also helps optimize the most efficient processing technique for any given manufactured product or process based upon volume, tooling, and capital requirements. When evaluating design and process alternatives, function analysis and/or TRIZ techniques may be applied to generate alternative concepts.

Applications of DFMA

A variety of methods may be used to apply DFMA properly to any given product or process. Generally, manual or software applications are the two most common approaches. In both approaches, the methodology seeks to find the minimum number of components or process steps required to perform the ultimate function requested by the customer, known as the highest order function, the goal, or the task for that product or process. Understanding the customer functions and requirements before the DFMA methodology is applied will result in the optimum design solution for any given product or process. If components and process steps can be eliminated, then they:

- Never have to be maintained in document control records.

- Do not have to be ordered, so no purchase order is required.

- Never have to be tracked by planning, scheduling, or traffic.

- Do not have to be received or inspected.

- Do not have to be dispositioned when discrepant, so no quality issues arise on components or processes eliminated.

- Are not shipped to or from the supplier, resulting in transportation savings.

- Do not have to be held in inventory, reducing Work in Process (WIP).

- Never arrive late from the supplier or create down time.

In addition to minimizing components and process steps, the DFMA process provides guidance to design teams on optimizing the product or process, reducing manufacturing and assembly costs, improving quality, and quantifying the improvements made through the DFMA methodology. It can also be used as a benchmarking tool to study competitors' products and processes and to quantify manufacturing and assembly difficulties. Finally, DFMA may also be used as a "should cost" tool to help validate design concepts, provide cost predictions, and negotiate supplier bids and contracts.

Teamwork—the Key to Success with DFMA

Just as in VM practice, teamwork is one of the keys to the success of DFMA. Because product design, material selection, and manufacturing processes are all discussed in a DFMA workshop or application, a properly populated, cross-functional team is the most effective method to maximize the benefits from any DFMA activity. Such a team should consist of members with experience in the following areas:

- Application (customer) engineering in order to understand customer requirements.

- Product design engineering.

- Process expertise in the process areas to be investigated.

- Manufacturing assembly and/or process engineering.

- Supplier development engineering in order to understand the processing capability of various suppliers.

- Design quality and/or process quality engineering.

- Program, launch, or operational management.

- Purchasing representation in order to verify suppliers' cost structures.

- Financial representation in order to verify labor and burden rates, etc.

- Packaging and/or industrial engineering for ergonomic issues.

- Other areas as needed for a particular business.

A DFMA cross-functional team established during the

early concept stage of a project can avoid crisis management in the final launch stages of that project. The cross-functional team empowers collective ownership of the design by manufacturing, engineering, and operations; it also serves as an excellent communication tool so that everyone involved has the opportunity to buy into the optimized design. In addition, teamwork minimizes the need for late design or process changes by ensuring that all team members concur with the design decisions. Finally, teamwork allows more effective responses to unexpected changes in product or customer requirements, if necessary, so that all team members, including the suppliers, know what is at stake.

Organizational Benefits of DFMA

Many organizational benefits may be achieved by implementing the DFMA methodology in the early concept stage of a new product or process.

Engineering-related benefits include, but are not limited to, such things as:

- Improved speed to market due to fewer engineering changes.

- Better use of time by engineers, who can spend more time making products and processes that can be manufactured and less time making changes in the launch or production phase of the project.

- Improved creativity by allowing engineers to focus on what they do best—exploration and innovation—using a very sophisticated "what if" tool.

- A lessons-learned library that can be tailored to individual products and processes with different labor, burden, and process conditions that may be documented, analyzed, and improved compared to the original.

Manufacturing (operations) benefits include, but are not limited to, such things as:

- Contributing more to design. DFMA promotes earlier involvement of operations personnel in design, which takes advantage of manufacturing/ process knowledge.

- Improved efficiency, with unnecessary steps, tools, and parts designed out of the production process.

- Improved product quality, with late changes and process steps, tooling, and components minimized. Therefore, products will be of higher quality since tooling will not have to be altered or even ordered, due to a simpler design.

- Better speed to market because products are produced more quickly due to streamlined manufacturing processes and simpler designs.

Management benefits include, but are not limited to, such things as:

- Improved total organizational cooperation. The cross-functional team approach provides metrics for discussion, tools for concurrent engineering, and support from all part of the company.

- World-class product development and manufacturing. Product design and operations use a structured, measurable, and efficient approach to optimize a solution per customer functions.

- Reduced cost. Products cost less to manufacture due to fewer tools, components, process steps, and optimized materials.

- A more competitive product. The marketing and sales staff has a better product to take to market and a more compelling story.

DFMA and Outsourcing

Typically, labor is only 4% of the cost of a component part. However, labor is normally the main reason that manufacturing organizations give when considering outsourcing. When properly implemented, DFMA can find savings in materials and manufacturing that more than make up for labor cost differences. If manufacturing operations can be kept local and cost competitive, then the risks of outsourcing can be avoided. These potential risks include:

- Costly engineering changes.

- Communication and cultural roadblocks.

- Quality problems or inadequate inspection methods.

- High shipping costs, including duty and/or taxes.

- Patent infringement.

If a manufacturing organization is compelled to outsource, then DFMA can be used to improve outsourcing opportunities by:

- Simplifying products so they are easier to manufacture, thus reducing long-distance engineering changes.

- Holding overseas suppliers accountable to best-practice costs, materials, and assembly methods.

- Optimizing material selection, which can reduce weight and thus shipping costs.

- Designing in quality from the start.

- Streamlining design-to-manufacturing development, which can help reduce communication problems.

Advantages of the DFMA Process

Up to 80% of the cost of a new part is locked in during the early design phases when material and manufacturing processes are defined. In the past, engineers relied on historical factors, such as previous experience, or turned the part over to purchasing after the design was finalized to find suppliers who could manufacture it using whatever process they were most familiar with. Unfortunately, this approach does not work with new designs, and changes made to cut costs after the tooling has started are very expensive. DFMA not only allows "pure" costing of materials and manufacturing techniques at the earliest of design phases, it also allows engineers to investigate the cost impact of alternate manufacturing processes that they may not even be familiar with. Here are some average reductions from real case studies that have been obtained with the application of DFMA:

Material/Manufacturing Technique	Average Cost Reduction (%)
Labor costs	42
Part count	54
Separate fasteners	57
Weight	22
Assembly time	60
Assembly cost	45
Assembly tools	73
Assembly operations	53
Product development	45
Total cost	50

Summary of the DFMA Methodology

The principle behind the DFMA methodology is that of reducing the part or process count of any given product or manufacturing system. Fewer parts or process steps generally result in:

- Fewer parts and processes that must obtain customer approval.
- Fewer and potentially simpler assembly stations required.
- Potentially less automatic assembly equipment required.
- Less dedicated supplier and fabrication tooling.
- Fewer fixtures and checking stations.
- Fewer assembly tools.
- The potential to eliminate testing or shorten overall testing time.

In addition to these benefits, the potential for enhanced product quality may be obtained with the reduction of part count due to:

- Fewer processing steps.
- Fewer adjustments.
- Fewer mating points or surfaces.
- Fewer tolerance stack-up problems.
- Fewer operator frustrations.
- Fewer material control problems.
- Fewer assembly fixtures.

By optimizing the design and process for any given product, which includes minimizing the part count and selecting the best material with the best manufacturing process for any given design, the lowest overall product cost may be achieved. This gives the best value to the customer and is why DFMA is a VM-related tool.

The DFMA methodology requires the design team to determine if a part is really required for the assembly by asking specific questions about each part as it is added in assembly sequence to the previous part. Every product must start with a base part, which is considered necessary. The next part to be added to the assembly must be a different material, require relative movement to the previous part, or be required for assembly purposes. If this next part does not meet any of these three criteria, then it is considered a potential candidate for elimination and is *not* included as a part in the minimum part count (a minimum part is one required for the assembly). If the next part that is added could be of the same material as the base part, does not need to move relative to the base part, or does not have to exist for assembly reasons, such as serviceability etc., then it is considered nonessential and could possibly be combined or integrated with the base part. All fasteners and connectors are automatically considered to be nonessential parts because there is always a method to eliminate these components. Maybe customer requirements will not allow this, but as far as the DFMA methodology is concerned, they are not included in the minimum part count for that assembly. This same procedure is then used for the remaining parts in the assembly in the order of assembly until all parts have been analyzed.

As each part is analyzed, assembly penalties are assigned to them based on the securing method to the previous part (e.g., threaded, snapped, crimped, staked), as well as penalties for handling difficulties (e.g., nest/tangle, bulky, flexible, difficult grasp) and insertion difficulties (e.g., restricted view, access, alignment, hold down required).

Finally, the alpha and beta symmetry is calculated for each part based on how many times the part must be rotated around its axis to be inserted onto the previous part (alpha symmetry) or how many times the part must be rotated around its other axis to be inserted correctly into the previous mating part (beta symmetry). For example, a round cylinder being inserted into a plate with a round hole would have an alpha symmetry of 180 degrees, meaning that either end of the cylinder could be inserted into the plate (180 degrees of rotation), and a beta symmetry of zero degrees because the cylinder is round, so it can be oriented into the plate in any direction when rotated around its diametrical axis.

Upon completion of this Design for Assembly (DFA) analysis time, penalties are equated to cost penalties and calculated for the total assembly. The Design for Manufacture (DFM) analysis uses cost models to determine the cost of various parts based on the material and process used for manufacture.

Conclusion

A number of references are offered for this methodology, (see the Selected Readings) but the universally accepted and most user-friendly, industry-tested tool for more than twenty-five years was developed by Boothroyd and Dewhurst, Inc., in a software package called Design for Assembly and Design for Manufacture (www.dfma. com). This software has many internal processes and cost models that help users optimize a design at a very early stage before complete drawings are even necessary. When used together, they can generate a total product cost for a given assembly with complete tooling costs, manufacturing costs, and labor costs broken down in detail. In addition, the software may be used as a "what if" tool by the design team to quickly determine the costs of alternative options once the initial design has been established. These options then can be quickly compared to determine the optimum solution based upon volume, available investment, available equipment, and many other factors.

Appendix G

Theory of Inventive Problem Solving

Introduction

Employed with VM, the Theory of Inventive Problem Solving (TRIZ) can be a very powerful technique. A trained professional can teach TRIZ during an actual VM study/workshop or as a separate exercise before or after the study team becomes engaged and when there is a specific problem that can't be solved with traditional brainstorming or other creativity techniques.

Background of TRIZ

TRIZ (the acronym is Russian) was originally created to guide problem solvers toward strong solutions to inventive problems. Today, TRIZ has evolved into a system that can be the cornerstone of innovation practice within business and the profession of VM. It was founded by Genrich Altshuller, a patent expert in the Soviet Navy in the 1940s whose job was to help inventors apply for patents. These inventors often asked him to assist in solving problems in addition to applying for patents. His curiosity about problem solving led him to search for standard methods. Altshuller felt an inventive method should be:

- A systematic, step-by-step procedure.

- A guide through a broad solution space to direct a repeatable and reliable ideal solution that is not dependent on psychological tools.

- Able to access the body of inventive knowledge.

- Able to add to the body of inventive knowledge.

- Familiar to inventors by following the same sort of approach used for problems where the solution is generally known.

Altshuller screened more than 200,000 patents looking for inventive problems and how they were solved. Of these, only 40,000 had somewhat inventive solutions and the rest were straightforward improvements. Altshuller defined an inventive problem as one in which an improvement in one feature causes another feature to degrade. This is known as a technical contradiction, and an example is increasing the wingspan of an aircraft, which causes additional weight and drag. Usually inventors resorted to compromise between contradicting features and thus never reached the ideal solution. In his study of patents, Altshuller found that many of them described a solution that eliminated or resolved the contradiction and did not require a compromise.

Altshuller also discovered patterns of invention in which the same fundamental problem or contradiction had been addressed by a number of inventions in different areas of technology. These same fundamental solutions were used over and over again, often separated by many years. Thus, a variety of problems from totally different technical areas could be solved with principles already known in another area of technology.

In addition to patterns of invention, Altshuller also found patterns of evolution. Engineering or technical systems don't evolve randomly, but rather according to objective patterns. These patterns may be retrieved from the patent database and purposefully used for system development without numerous blind trial and error approaches.

Altshuller categorized patents into five levels according to the problem solving process as shown in the table on page 139.

Level	Degree of Inventiveness	Percent Solutions	Source of Knowledge	Approximate Number of Solutions to Consider
1	Apparent solution	32	Personal knowledge	10
2	Minor improvement	45	Knowledge within company	100
3	Major improvement	18	Knowledge within the industry	1000
4	New concept	4	Knowledge outside the industry	100,000
5	Discovery	1	All that is knowable	1,000,000

Each succeeding level requires broader knowledge and the consideration of more solutions before an ideal solution is reached. During the process, Altshuller found that the majority of the same problems had been solved using one of only forty fundamental inventive principles; he also realized that more than 90% of problems faced had been solved somewhere previously. He discovered that most of the solutions could be derived from knowledge already present at the lower levels, thus leaving few problems that needed to be solved at the higher levels.

Fundamentals of the TRIZ Methodology

TRIZ uses resources that are often overlooked coupled with traditional brainstorming and similar techniques. These resources are functional, energy fields, information, substances, space, and time, as defined below:

- Functional—The capability of a system or its surroundings to perform additional functions, including super-effects or unexpected benefits that arise as a result of innovation.

- Energy fields—Any kind of energy, action, force, etc., available in the system or its environment, such as mechanical, thermal, chemical, electrical, magnetic, or electromagnetic.

- Information—Any additional information about the system, which can be obtained with the help of dissipation fields or the matter of fields passing through the system.

- Substances—Any kind of material that composes the system or its surroundings.

- Space—Free, unoccupied space that exists in a system or its surroundings.

- Time—Time intervals before the start, after the finish, and between the cycles of a technological process, which are partially or completely unused.

During the first phase of the TRIZ process, all of the above resources need to be evaluated thoroughly as the cross-functional workshop team describes the problem. All of the resources of the system and sub-systems to be studied, as well as their mutual relationships to each other, need to be fully analyzed to ensure that a solution doesn't already exist within the information known collectively by the workshop team.

Additional items that should be gathered in this first phase of the TRIZ process are:

- Voice of the customer information (sales, marketing, or other QFD needs).

- A clear statement of the problem, target cost goal, or quality issue in specific terms.

- Any supporting documents of the problem or concern to be analyzed.

- All supporting product, process, or system drawings or sketches of the problem.

- Warranty data, field returns, and/or test results of the specific problem.

- Any competitive analysis information that relates to the concern or problem.

Next, it is important to propose an ideal vision of the solution to the problem being studied, assuming there are no strings attached. In other words, in an ideal world, what might the solution look like? Ideality in TRIZ terms is a measure of all useful functions divided by all harmful or undesired functions. By understanding the ideal solution, a clearer picture of the evolutionary goal of ideality becomes more evident. With this definition in mind, the *ideal system* performs a required function without actually existing. Thus, the function is often performed using existing resources. This is why it is imperative to clearly define all of the existing resources as listed above.

Another important principle in the first phase of a TRIZ workshop is understanding what the allowable changes to the system are. Depending on the development phase of the product or process being studied, certain changes may or may not be allowed based on customer acceptance criteria, financial payback, or program timing. It is important to understand these facts before the actual TRIZ process is started because it is very frustrating to come up with an ideal solution that no one will support. Along with this principle comes another similar one that simply states that concurrence needs to be reached on the criteria for selecting solution concepts before the workshop begins. Without these agreed-upon criteria, the final selection process for concepts may be a real challenge and may not be supported by the management team.

Finally, it is important to understand the company business environment for the product or process being studied. Is capital available to accomplish the proposed solution, or is the change customer-driven and a solution must be found at any cost? These and other similar things are critical for the team to understand and respect as they use the TRIZ methodology.

The second phase of the TRIZ methodology is to formulate the problem in terms of physical contradictions and identify both the useful and harmful effects. There are a variety of ways that this may be done, but one method is to create a block diagram with useful functions and harmful functions and link them together with lines indicating:

- Does the selected function *produce* another function?

- Does the selected function *counteract* another function?

- Is the selected function *produced by* another function?

- Is the selected function *counteracted* by another function?

By completing this functional block diagram, various problems can be identified, and technical conflicts that might force a compromise are outlined visually. Functional block diagramming performed as a team exercise may actually result in a solution that can be achieved at a lower level than originally thought, thus reducing the complexity and length of the study.

The third phase of the TRIZ methodology involves finding possible ways to resolve conflicting functions or contradictions, as demonstrated in the functional block diagram of useful and harmful functions. After studying more than 1.5 million patents worldwide, Altshuller extracted thirty-nine standard technical characteristics that cause conflict, known as the 39 Engineering Parameters shown in the table on page 144.

While extracting the 39 Engineering Parameters, Altshuller also developed the 40 Inventive Principles, which help to find a highly inventive solution to any given problem. To indicate which of these principles is likely to give a satisfactory result, Altshuller created the Table of Contradictions, which lists the 39 Engineering Parameters on the x-axis as the undesirable secondary effects, while on the y-axis is the feature to improve. In the intersecting cells, the appropriate inventive principles to use for a solution are listed. The whole table is too extensive to present here properly, so only a portion of it is shown on page 145 to give you an idea of how it might be used.

39 Engineering Parameters

1. Weight of moving object	14. Strength
2. Weight of non-moving object	15. Durability of moving object
3. Length of moving object	16. Durability of non-moving object
4. Length of non-moving object	17. Temperature
5. Area of moving object	18. Brightness
6. Area of non-moving object	19. Energy spent by moving object
7. Volume of moving object	20. Energy spent by non-moving object
8. Volume of non-moving object	21. Power
9. Speed	22. Waste of energy
10. Force	23. Waste of substance
11. Tension, pressure, stress	24. Loss of information
12. Shape	25. Waste of time
13. Stability of object	26. Amount of substance
	27. Reliability
	28. Accuracy of measurement
	29. Accuracy of manufacturing
	30. Harmful factors acting on object
	31. Harmful side effects
	32. Manufacturability
	33. Convenience of use
	34. Repairability
	35. Adaptability
	36. Complexity of device
	37. Complexity of control
	38. Level of automation
	39. Productivity

Table of Contradictions

Feature to Improve / Undesired Result (Conflict)	1 Weight of moving object	2 Weight of non-moving object	3 Length of moving object	4 Length of non-moving object	5 Area of moving object	6 Area of non-moving object	7 Volume of moving object	8 Volume of non-moving object	9 Speed	10 Force
30 Harmful factors acting on object										
31 Harmful side effects										
32 Manufacturability										
33 Convenience of use										
34 Repairability										
35 Adaptability										
36 Complexity of device										
37 Complexity of control										
38 Level of automation										
39 Productivity										

Once all of the inventive principles are noted in the intersecting cells (and note that not all intersecting cells will lead to a solution), the results of these cells are then placed into Altshuller's 40 Inventive Principles table, which will show corresponding answers or things to try that may lead to a possible solution. This can be accomplished with greater speed and efficiency today using software tools, which have an extensive database of knowledge based on these forty inventive principles. Whether software tools are used or not, TRIZ allows us to channel our creativity by reviewing multiple solutions for a particular problem, many of which have already been encountered by someone at some point.

TRIZ as a Value Management Tool

You may include TRIZ as either a Six Sigma tool or a VM tool to enhance brainstorming techniques. TRIZ works well because chosen trials follow the patterns of technological system evolution that has been in existence for hundreds of years.

TRIZ has been used as a VM tool to solve technically challenging problems and to develop new concepts for future products and processes to generate new, truly creative ideas. For example, during one VM workshop with a cross-functional team, the study team members exhausted all of the ideas that they could collectively generate after about four hours of brainstorming. However, as an experiment, after a brief introduction to TRIZ, this same study team spent just one additional hour using the TRIZ approach. Ten additional ideas were generated, two of which were developed into concepts where viable business cases were completed. This reinforces the fact that the TRIZ approach can definitely expand the creativity of a group of individuals due to the fact that an extensive knowledge base can be tapped into.

Conclusion

TRIZ has many similarities to VM in that both evaluate the problem, product, or process from a function point of view rather than just evaluating another component to replace the current component. The component you are evaluating may not be necessary, or it may be combined with another component, and TRIZ along with VM can help reveal that fact. TRIZ is not a replacement for VM, but rather a tool for enhancement that can help with difficult problems, or where a totally new concept or next generation product or process is required. TRIZ will help your organization take that quantum leap to the development of tomorrow's product or process, going a step beyond just improving the existing one. It can also enhance the VM methodology by producing results that might not be revealed with other well-known creativity techniques.

Appendix H

Tear-Down Analysis

Tear-down analysis not only involves analyzing and benchmarking competitive products for function, but also evaluating materials, manufacturing processes, and assembly times. The VA/VM team needs to have knowledge of the best technology, materials, and processes worldwide in order to provide products with the highest value to the customer.

The U.S. auto industry was one of the first implementers of product tear-down in the 1960s. Competitive vehicles were reviewed for initial defects, tested and operated for thousands of miles over various roads. Failures that occurred during testing and operation were reviewed. The vehicles were then torn down and the parts displayed on tables in a large building. Engineers, manufacturing experts, and marketing personnel were invited to review and analyze the parts for ideas and best practice concepts.

General Motors introduced the static tear-down method to Isuzu in the early 1970s. Isuzu further refined the tear-down process and incorporated it into their VA/VM process. Yoshihiko Sato from Isuzu presented a paper on tear-down analysis at the 1989 SAVE VE conference. Then Sato and J. Jerry Kaufman published a book on VA tear-down in 2005.

There are several types of tear-down analysis. The features of the various types can be combined to meet specific requirements. The more common types are:

- Static tear-down.
  - Parts are removed without recording disassembly or reassembly times.
  - Dimensions and weights of parts are typically recorded before they are put on display.
- Dynamic tear-down.
  - Disassembly times are recorded.
  - Assembly times can be recorded when parts are reassembled.
- Cost tear-down.
  - Costs are estimated for all parts.
  - Costing software can be used to estimate the part costs.
  - Suppliers can participate to provide cost estimates.
- Material tear-down.
  - Materials are identified for all the parts.
  - Finishes and heat treatment operations are identified.
- Process tear-down.
  - Manufacturing processes are identified for all the parts.
- Matrix tear-down.
  - Similar systems from different internal product lines are evaluated for VA/VE ideas, e.g., instrument panels from different types of construction equipment are evaluated for common parts.

The following steps are typically used in the tear-down analysis:

1. **Identify the purpose of the tear-down and conduct planning.**

   - The purpose is typically to generate VA/VM ideas to provide functions at lower cost, increase performance, improve quality, and establish target costs.

   - Planning should include developing tear-down procedures and data collection forms if they do not already exist.

2. **Identify and obtain resources, facilities, tools, and personnel for the tear-down process.**

   - It is ideal if a permanent tear-down and display room can be established.

   - The tear-down leader and facilitator should have training in tear-down methods.

   - Responsibility lists should be developed for all personnel involved in the tear-down team.

3. **Identify the competitors and acquire the products for tear-down.**

   - Products are typically from the top competitors.

   - New models recently introduced in the market are good candidates.

   - Also consider international products that may have unique functions unavailable in the domestic market.

   - Conduct tests, such as performance, noise, cooling, and so on, on products before tear-down.

   - Customer input from the voice of the customer/QFD can be used to determine which tests are important.

4. **Disassemble the product and record data, including video and digital photos.**

- All parts should be logged and tagged.

- Parts can be reassembled to obtain assembly times.

- Use different color tags for different products if you are tearing down more than one product.

5. **Display torn-down parts and obtain comments from additional personnel.**

- Comments and ideas from various employees, experts, suppliers, etc., are typically obtained within one week of the tear-down.

- It is good if parts can be left on permanent display until they are replaced with the new competitive model. That way, VA/VM teams and engineering, manufacturing, and sourcing personnel can visit the tear-down room whenever they are working on related projects.

6. **Analyze data.**

- Analyze the data to identify new materials and processes.

- Determine the best approach to provide the highest value for functions.

- Establish best-in-class competitors by function.

- Generate VA/VM ideas.

7. **Publish and use results.**

- The information can be published on CDs or an internal web page for future reference.

- Clicking on the parts in the database can activate links to videos and digital photos of the parts.

- Information can be stored in DFMA databases.

- Ideas generated can be used for VA on existing products and VM on new products.

- The cost information can be used to help develop target costs.

- Information from the tear-down can be used in the QFD house of quality matrix.

Appendix I

Weighted Evaluation Technique

The purpose of the weighted evaluation technique is to provide a more objective method to evaluate subjective attributes and rank competing ideas for consideration. Weighted evaluation is a two-step procedure. In step 1, the team determines the criteria or attributes against which to evaluate each idea. Then team members determine how much importance each one will have in choosing the best idea. In step 2, the team lists all the ideas and evaluates them against each attribute, then scores and ranks them.

Step 1—Determining Criteria and Weights

1. **Determine the subjective criteria or attributes for evaluating your proposals.**

   - The attributes, features, or criteria you pick normally relate to the subject of the study. For example, a manufactured product might be judged on its reliability, durability, ease to manufacture, development effort, customer acceptance, and so on. A car might be judged on its handling, style, acceleration, operating cost, and so on.

   - Each criterion used should meet minimum user or owner needs. That is, if safety is being compared to cost, the comparison is not between unsafe conditions versus lower costs, but increased safety over the minimum required safety versus cost.

• Cost may be a criterion, but it is not recommended since all proposals must also pass a business case evaluation.

2. **Define the criteria so all team members understand them.**

   • The more elements of criteria that are compared to each other, the better. This reduces the chance that one or two elements will receive such weight that they swing or govern the decision regardless of how the other elements score. Do not stack the deck!

3. **List all the criteria on the evaluation form, assigning each a letter of the alphabet as shown in the figure.**

4. **Use a paired comparison to determine the weight to be used for each criterion.** Paired comparison is a technique based on the understanding that any one person or group of people can select between any two items, or, if they cannot choose, can call them equal in importance.

   • Prepare a scoring matrix (as shown on page 155).

   • Compare each criterion to another in turn. First, ask which is more important, A or B. In the example of initial cost versus maintenance, the answer is A.

   • Next, ask how much more important that answer is, rating it major, medium, or minor—that is, giving it three, two, or one points. Again, in the example, initial cost A is medium in being more important than maintenance and is thus recorded in the scoring matrix as A-2.

   • Continue to compare A with C, then A with D, and so on, until all criteria are compared with each other and recorded in terms of their importance. Note that, in the example, when B is compared with C, a choice cannot be made between them, so the selection is recorded in the scoring matrix as B/C.

Determining the Weights

JUDICIAL PHASE	
STUDY TITLE HVAC – Small Office	**DETERMINING WEIGHTS FOR EVALUATION**

	GOALS, DESIRED CRITERIA, FUNCTIONS, FEATURES	RAW SCORE	ASSIGNED WEIGHT
A	Initial Cost	8	10
B	Maintenance	5	6
C	Energy Usage	6	8
D	Aesthetics	1	1
E	Reliability/Performance	5	6
F			
G			
H			

SCORING MATRIX

	B	C	D	E	F	G	H	I
A	A-2	A/C	A-2	A-3				
B		B/C	B-3	B/E				
C			C-3	C/E				
D				E-3				
E								
F								
G								
H								

HOW IMPORTANT
3 – Major preference
2 – Medium preference
1 – Minor preference

> All judgments of the relative importance of criteria are between minimum and maximum performance levels, or between needs and desires, with the intent to determine the relative importance of each in order to optimize them later or make tradeoffs.

5. **Add the total number of each letter of the alphabet recorded in the scoring matrix.** This is the raw score of the weight for each of the criteria selected.

> If one criterion receives a zero score, it means that the attribute is not important to the team in evaluating the idea, and it can be dropped from further consideration. If, however, the team disagrees with this automatic conclusion, the evaluation criteria can be saved by giving it a raw score of one.

6. **Reviewing the raw score, determine the weight of importance of each of the criteria on a scale of one to ten, with ten being the highest and one being the lowest.** Remember that not all criteria are created equal.

Step 2—Rank Each Idea

1. **List each idea on an evaluation matrix similar to that shown in the figure on page 157.** Be sure to list the current idea or present way as the first idea on the list. This is the one that you are comparing with your new ideas.

Ranking Ideas

EVALUATION MATRIX

IDEAS	WT	Initial Cost (10)	Maintenance (6)	Energy Usage (8)	Aesthetics (1)	Reliability Perfor. (6)	TOTAL
PRESENT WAY: One rooftop unit over mech. room	5	E	E	E	E	E	RANK
	4	VG	VG	VG	VG	VG	
	3	G	(G)	G	(G)	G	**5**
	2	F	F	(F)	F	(F)	
	1	(P)	P	P	P	P	
	SUB TOT	10	18	16	3	12	59
IDEA 1: One thru-wall One rooftop	5	(E)	E	E	E	E	RANK
	4	VG	VG	VG	VG	VG	
	3	G	G	G	(G)	(G)	**1**
	2	F	(F)	(F)	F	F	
	1	P	P	P	P	P	
	SUB TOT	50	12	16	3	18	99
IDEA 2: One rooftop One floor mtd.	5	E	E	E	E	E	RANK
	4	VG	VG	VG	VG	VG	
	3	(G)	G	G	G	(G)	**4**
	2	F	F	(F)	(F)	F	
	1	P	(P)	P	P	P	
	SUB TOT	30	6	16	2	18	72
IDEA 3: Two thru-walls	5	E	E	E	E	E	RANK
	4	VG	VG	VG	VG	VG	
	3	G	(G)	(G)	(G)	(G)	**3**
	2	(F)	F	F	F	F	
	1	P	P	P	P	P	
	SUB TOT	20	18	24	3	18	83
IDEA 4: Modify existing design	5	E	E	E	E	E	RANK
	4	(VG)	VG	VG	(VG)	VG	
	3	G	(G)	G	G	G	**2**
	2	F	F	(F)	F	(F)	
	1	P	P	P	P	P	
	SUB TOT	40	18	16	4	12	90
IDEA 5:	5	E	E	E	E	E	RANK
	4	VG	VG	VG	VG	VG	
	3	G	G	G	G	G	
	2	F	F	F	F	F	
	1	P	P	P	P	P	
	SUB TOT						

GOALS, DESIRED CRITERIA FEATURES — ASSIGNED VALUE

Seek the best, not perfection!

2. List the criteria and the weights you have just established across the top of the form.

3. Take one criterion at a time and score all ideas against it.
   - Score each idea as:
     - Excellent—five points.
     - Very good—four points.
     - Good—three points.
     - Fair—two points.
     - Poor—one point.
   - Multiply each idea's score against the assigned weight at the top of the page and record the subtotal as shown.

4. After each of the criteria is scored, one at a time and in turn, add up the subtotals of each and record the raw score as shown.

5. The preferred solution with the highest score is ranked first, with the next lowest ranked second, and so on. In the example, note that the present way is ranked fifth out of five. That means that any idea on the list is preferred.

> If the team wants to press on with an idea that does not come out with as good a rank as the team expected, then analyze what causes that effect and brainstorm ways to mitigate it during its development and presentation. A low score could indicate potential roadblocks from future decision makers.

Appendix J

Leadership in Energy and Environmental Design (Sustainability) Checklist

Introduction

The Leadership in Energy and Environmental Design (LEED) checklist, first developed by the U.S. Green Building Council (USGBC) in 1999, is a useful tool to employ during the creative phase to identify ideas for improving building sustainability (green buildings). It is also a valuable tool to owners interested in lowering life-cycle costs (see Appendix K, Life Cycle Costing). The USGBC has prepared various checklists, such as new construction and major renovation (NC), existing building (EB), commercial interiors (CI), core and shell (CS), homes (H), and neighborhood development (ND). These checklists and further information can be found on the USGBC web site, www.usgbc.org.

The goal of this process is to create buildings that meet the needs of current building occupants while being mindful of the needs of future generations. Green building design includes all stakeholders in the project, i.e., the design team (owners, architects, engineers, and value specialists), the contractors, the maintenance staff, and the building occupants.

Green building practices can substantially reduce negative environmental impacts and reverse the trend of unsustainable construction practices. As an added benefit, green design measures reduce operating costs, enhance building marketability, increase worker productivity, and reduce potential liability resulting from indoor air quality problems.

LEED Rating System

The LEED rating system is based on proven technology. It evaluates environmental performance from a whole-building perspective over a building's life cycle, providing a definitive standard for what constitutes a green building.

As an example, the LEED NC categories and points are:

- Sustainable sites—14 possible points.
- Water efficiency—5 possible points.
- Energy and atmosphere—17 possible points.
- Materials and resources—13 possible points.
- Indoor environmental quality—14 possible points.
- Innovation and design process—5 possible points.

The USGBC has developed a certification review process to certify buildings per the checklist.

The certification levels are:

- Certified—26 to 32 points.
- Silver—33 to 38 points.
- Gold—39 to 51 points.
- Platinum—52 or more points.

The USGBC has also developed a LEED Accredited Professional training program for those interested in becoming more familiar with the program.

Appendix K

Life Cycle Costing

Introduction

Life cycle costing (LCC) can be defined as "an economic assessment of competing design alternatives, considering all significant costs over the economic life of each alternative, expressed in equivalent dollars."

A simple example illustrates the application of life cycle cost principles. Say that a hospital corporation is considering two alternatives for a nursing-care addition to an existing building. One requires a greater initial investment because it relies on the use of automated patient monitoring and recording systems. The second option is less expensive in terms of initial costs because it relies on conventional data collection technology. The question arises, "Do the long-term savings in operating expenses (nurses' salaries) associated with the first solution justify the initial capital investment over the life of the building?"

In order to answer this question, the decisionmaker first needs to use the principles of life cycle costing to remove any factors that might have the same impact in any given design solution from consideration. This reduces the complexity of the analysis since it focuses the decisionmaker's attention on design variables that represent significant fluctuations in long-term costs. Second, the most critical costs associated with each alternative are isolated and computed. The automated nursing system would have higher capital, operation, and maintenance costs than a conventional design but would result in lower functional-use costs in terms of staff salaries. The costs for each alternative are grouped by year over the expected life of the building, and anticipated replacement, alteration, and salvage costs estimated. Third, all costs are converted to a common economic point of reference by using an appropriate discount factor. This discounting is done because a cost incurred at any given point in the future of a building's life cycle does not have the same impact as it might have if it were incurred today due to interest rates, inflation, and other economic variables. Finally, discounted costs for each alternative are summed up and solutions ranked in terms of life cycle cost impact. It may be necessary at this point to perform a number of separate analyses in order to test the validity of this ranking. Although the final selection of an alternative will probably be based on economic variables, the effects of noneconomic factors, such as a design's functional and technological feasibility, must be considered as well.

The process begins with input data based on programmatic and client-defined information, in addition to economic constraints associated with local cost factors, interest rates, and tax credits. Next, input data for specific components of the item under study, such as initial costs, operation and maintenance costs, and energy factors, are enumerated for each alternative. These costs are then computed and predicted using discounting methods, and careful considerations of noneconomic design variables are made to temper the ranking of the alternative solutions.

Economic Principles

Life cycle costing is based on the major economic principles of the time value of money, the equivalence approach, and the type of economic decision to be made. The concept of time value of money is based on the notion that money has earning power that accrues to its investor over time. On the other hand, for the borrower, a continuing or periodic cost offsets this earning power. Because of the earning power or cost of money, dollars spent in the future do not equal dollars spent today. For purposes of comparing these dollars, the concept of equivalence allows monies spent over time to be brought to a common basis.

Time Value of Money

The value of money is time dependent because money can be invested over time to yield a return. This is true for both the investor and the borrower. For this reason, a dollar amount today will be worth more than that same dollar amount in a year's time. For example, if $100 were deposited in a savings account paying 7% annual interest compounded annually, it would grow to $100 x $1.07 = $107.00 by the end of the first year, to $100 x ($1.07)^2 = $114.49 by the end of the second year, and to $100 x ($1.07)^3 = $122.50 by the end of the third year.

Present Worth or Net Present Value Method

The most common method of calculating the effects of the time value of money is the present worth (PW) method, also referred to as the net present value (NPV) method, which converts all present and future costs to a common reference point, namely, the value of money today. Because initial costs are expressed in today's dollars, this method converts long-term or recurring costs that will come up during the life of the item being studied to a single, present worth value. The interest rate is referred to as the "discount rate" in life cycle costing. The table on page 164 shows the single, present worth of a monetary value now and over future years.

Present Worth: Compound Interest Factors, Single Payment (PW)

Years	6% Present Worth	7% Present Worth	8% Present Worth	9% Present Worth	10% Present Worth	12% Present Worth
1	0.94340	0.93458	0.92593	0.91743	0.90909	0.89286
2	0.89000	0.87344	0.85734	0.84168	0.82645	0.79719
3	0.83962	0.81630	0.79383	0.77218	0.75131	0.71178
4	0.79209	0.76290	0.73503	0.70843	0.68301	0.63552
5	0.74726	0.71299	0.68058	0.64993	0.62092	0.56743
6	0.70496	0.66634	0.63017	0.59627	0.56447	0.50663
7	0.66506	0.62275	0.58349	0.54703	0.51316	0.45235
8	0.62741	0.58201	0.54027	0.50187	0.46651	0.40388
9	0.59190	0.54393	0.50025	0.46043	0.42410	0.36061
10	0.55839	0.50835	0.46319	0.42241	0.38554	0.32197
11	0.52679	0.47509	0.42888	0.38753	0.35049	0.28748
12	0.49697	0.44401	0.39711	0.35553	0.31863	0.25668
13	0.46884	0.41496	0.36770	0.32618	0.28966	0.22917
14	0.44230	0.38782	0.34046	0.29925	0.26333	0.20462
15	0.41727	0.36245	0.31524	0.27454	0.23939	0.18270
16	0.39365	0.33873	0.29189	0.25187	0.21763	0.16312
17	0.37136	0.31657	0.27027	0.23107	0.19784	0.14564
18	0.35034	0.29586	0.25025	0.21199	0.17986	0.13004
19	0.33051	0.27651	0.23171	0.19449	0.16351	0.11611
20	0.31180	0.25842	0.21455	0.17843	0.14864	0.10367
21	0.29416	0.24151	0.19866	0.16370	0.13513	0.09256
22	0.27751	0.22571	0.18394	0.15018	0.12285	0.08264
23	0.26180	0.21095	0.17032	0.13778	0.11168	0.07379
24	0.24698	0.19715	0.15770	0.12640	0.10153	0.06588
25	0.23300	0.18425	0.14602	0.11597	0.09230	0.05882
26	0.21981	0.17220	0.13520	0.10639	0.08391	0.05252
27	0.20737	0.16093	0.12519	0.09761	0.07628	0.04689
28	0.19563	0.15040	0.11591	0.08955	0.06934	0.04187
29	0.18456	0.14056	0.10733	0.08215	0.06304	0.03738
30	0.17411	0.13137	0.09938	0.07537	0.05731	0.03338
31	0.16425	0.12277	0.09202	0.06915	0.05210	0.02980
32	0.15496	0.11474	0.08520	0.06344	0.04736	0.02661
33	0.14619	0.10723	0.07889	0.05820	0.04306	0.02376
34	0.13791	0.10022	0.07305	0.05339	0.03914	0.02121
35	0.13011	0.09366	0.06763	0.04899	0.03558	0.01894
36	0.12274	0.08754	0.06262	0.04494	0.03235	0.01691
37	0.11579	0.08181	0.05799	0.04123	0.02941	0.01510
38	0.10924	0.07646	0.05369	0.03783	0.02673	0.01348
39	0.10306	0.07146	0.04971	0.03470	0.02430	0.01204
40	0.09722	0.06678	0.04603	0.03184	0.02209	0.01075

The formula for this table is:

$$PW = F\left(1/(1+i)^n\right), \text{ where}$$

F is the future amount.

i is the interest (discount) rate.

n is the number of years.

The table on page 166 shows the effect of a uniform series of payments (present worth annuity, or PWA) converted to a single equivalent amount.

The formula for this table is:

$$PWA = A\left(\left((1+i)^n - 1\right)/\left(i(1+i)^n\right)\right), \text{ where}$$

A is the annual amount.

i is the interest (discount) rate.

n is the number of years.

Discount Rate

The discount, or interest, rate is the time value of money. It is commonly established as the nominal rate of increase in the value of money over time after subtracting the effects of inflation. The discount rate for a federal government study might be 7%, and for private industry, 10% or more. Private industry discount rates are higher than government rates because shareholders require a high return on their money.

The amount of project risk is also sometimes reflected in the discount rate. For federal government rates, refer to OMB Circular A-94, dated May 21, 1993, and published in the federal register on June 14, 1993. This document states that constant dollar costs should use a real U.S. Treasury borrowing rate on marketable securities of comparable maturity to the period of life cycle cost analysis (see Appendix C, OMB Circular A-94, for a table of discount rates which are updated annually).

Present Worth of Annuity: Compound Interest Factors (PWA)

Years	6% Present Worth	7% Present Worth	8% Present Worth	9% Present Worth	10% Present Worth	12% Present Worth
1	0.9434	0.9346	0.9259	0.9174	0.9091	0.8929
2	1.8334	1.8080	1.7833	1.7591	1.7355	1.6901
3	2.6730	2.6243	2.5771	2.5313	2.4869	2.4018
4	3.4651	3.3872	3.3121	3.2397	3.1699	3.0373
5	4.2124	4.1002	3.9927	3.8897	3.7908	3.6048
6	4.9173	4.7665	4.6229	4.4859	4.3553	4.1114
7	5.5824	5.3893	5.2064	5.0330	4.8684	4.5638
8	6.2098	5.9713	5.7466	5.5348	5.3349	4.9676
9	6.8017	6.5152	6.2469	5.9952	5.7590	5.3282
10	7.3601	7.0236	6.7101	6.4177	6.1446	5.6502
11	7.8869	7.4987	7.1390	6.8052	6.4951	5.9377
12	8.3838	7.9427	7.5361	7.1607	6.8137	6.1944
13	8.8527	8.3577	7.9038	7.4869	7.1034	6.4235
14	9.2950	8.7455	8.2442	7.7862	7.3667	6.6282
15	9.7122	9.1079	8.5595	8.0607	7.6061	6.8109
16	10.1059	9.4466	8.8514	8.3126	7.8237	6.9740
17	10.4773	9.7632	9.1216	8.5436	8.0216	7.1196
18	10.8276	10.0591	9.3719	8.7556	8.2014	7.2497
19	11.1581	10.3356	9.6036	8.9501	8.3649	7.3658
20	11.4699	10.5940	9.8181	9.1285	8.5136	7.4694
21	11.7641	10.8355	10.0168	9.2922	8.6487	7.5620
22	12.0416	11.0612	10.2007	9.4424	8.7715	7.6446
23	12.3034	11.2722	10.3711	9.5802	8.8832	7.7184
24	12.5504	11.4693	10.5288	9.7066	8.9847	7.7843
25	12.7834	11.6536	10.6748	9.8226	9.0770	7.8431
26	13.0032	11.8258	10.8100	9.9290	9.1609	7.8957
27	13.2105	11.9867	10.9352	10.0266	9.2372	7.9426
28	13.4062	12.1371	11.0511	10.1161	9.3066	7.9844
29	13.5907	12.2777	11.1584	10.1983	9.3696	8.0218
30	13.7648	12.4090	11.2578	10.2737	9.4269	8.0552
31	13.9291	12.5318	11.3498	10.3428	9.4790	8.0850
32	14.0840	12.6466	11.4350	10.4062	9.5264	8.1116
33	14.2302	12.7538	11.5139	10.4644	9.5694	8.1354
34	14.3681	12.8540	11.5869	10.5178	9.6086	8.1566
35	14.4982	12.9477	11.6546	10.5668	9.6442	8.1755
36	14.6210	13.0352	11.7172	10.6118	9.6765	8.1924
37	14.7368	13.1170	11.7752	10.6530	9.7059	8.2075
38	14.8460	13.1935	11.8289	10.6908	9.7327	8.2210
39	14.9491	13.2649	11.8786	10.7255	9.7570	8.2330
40	15.0463	13.3317	11.9246	10.7574	9.7791	8.2438

Analysis Period or Life Cycle

The analysis period, or life cycle, is also a key element in life cycle cost analysis. It is the time frame selected to compare alternatives in order to determine which is more economical for a particular application. Normally, a life cycle cost analysis is based on a life cycle period of between twenty-five and forty years. The U.S. military uses twenty-five years for buildings and one hundred years for civil works. Whether a short or long time frame is selected, the same life cycle cost approach is used. Thus, the selection of the analysis period will depend to a large extent on the owner's objectives and perspectives or on established organizational policy.

Present Time

The present time in a life cycle cost analysis marks the beginning point of a series of expenditures. For PW analysis, it also represents the point at which all life cycle costs are combined (by discounting), compared, and analyzed.

Costs

The value specialist needs to consider various costs and cost relationships, the proper understanding of which is essential to the completion of an effective life cycle cost analysis. Costs incurred prior to an analysis are called "sunk costs" and are never included in life cycle costing. To avoid the impact of inflation, all costs should be stated in "constant dollars," that is, without the effects of inflation and based on the purchasing power of the dollar for the particular year considered the present time.

All costs attributable to an alternative are considered in any life cycle cost analysis. These include initial procurement costs at the beginning of the analysis period; disposal, demolition, and other salvage costs at the end;

and costs incurred between those times. Whether any particular type of cost should be included depends primarily on two factors: (1) whether that type of cost is relevant for the particular item under study, and (2) whether the projected magnitude of that type of cost is significant in comparison to other relevant costs for the life cycle cost analysis. For convenience, these costs have been divided into the following categories:

- Initial investment costs.
- Replacement and major repair costs.
- Salvage (terminal) costs.
- Maintenance, repair, and custodial costs.
- Energy costs.
- Other types of costs, such as staffing, insurance, tax elements, and so forth.

Monetary benefits, which are normally considered as negative costs in the life cycle cost analysis, include all benefits that can be readily quantified in terms of dollars, such as salvage values, and other forms of income, cost reduction, and marketable by-products. The decision as to whether any particular monetary benefit should be included in an analysis is usually based on relevance and significance.

Present Worth Method Example

To illustrate the principles of life cycle costing, the below example outlines the process of performing the analysis.

Large Screen, High Definition TVs

Consider the selection among three large screen, high definition TVs, with a 6% discount rate and a twelve-year life cycle. Other relevant data are:

Type of Cost	Alternative 1 42" DLP HDTV	Alternative 2 42" Plasma HDTV	Alternative 3 46" LCD HDTV
Initial cost	$1,700	$2,300	$3,300
Contract maintenance (annual)	120	90	140
Electric energy (annual)	120	80	100
Useful life	6 years	8 years	12 years

Each cost element is entered on the PW format worksheet (see the figure above). This worksheet is divided into three major categories. The upper third is devoted to initial costs. In this example, the purchase cost is listed for each TV. Note that the estimated cost and the PW cost are the same for the initial cost category. The total initial cost for each alternative is then determined and recorded in the appropriate place on the form.

The middle third of the worksheet is used for recording replacement and salvage values.

When an alternative has a shorter or longer life than the life cycle specified, an adjustment for the unequal life is necessary. If the life of an alternative is shorter than the project's life cycle, the item continues to be replaced until the life cycle is reached. On the other hand, if the item's life is longer than the specified life cycle, a terminal or salvage value for the item is recognized at the end of the life cycle. This treatment, using the PW factors from the table on page 164, illustrated as follows:

- Alternative 1: replacement (n = 6) = $1,700 x (0.7050) = $1,198
- Alternative 2: replacement (n = 8) = $2,300 x (0.6274) = $1,443

- Alternative 3: salvage (n = 12) = $1,150 x (0.4970) = $571

The salvage value for alternatives 1 and 2 equals zero since they both complete replacement cycles at the end of the twelve-year life cycle.

The final effort requires converting all annual or recurring costs to the present time. Using the PWA factor (see the table on page 166), the recurring costs of contract maintenance would be:

- Alternative 1: maintenance (PW) = $120 x (8.384) = $1,006
- Alternative 2: maintenance (PW) = $90 x (8.384) = $755
- Alternative 3: maintenance (PW) = $140 x (8.384) = $1,174

According to this table, the PW of the energy costs for each alternative would be:

- Alternative 1: energy (PW) = $120 x (8.384) = $1,006
- Alternative 2: energy (PW) = $80 x (8.384) = $671
- Alternative 3: energy (PW) = $100 x (8.384) = $838

A summary of PW life cycle costs is shown in the figure on page 171.

The total PW life cycle cost for each TV is established by totaling the initial, replacement/salvage, and annual operating costs. As a result of life cycle costing, one can see that, although alternative 2 was initially higher in cost than alternative 1, it costs much less to operate. These calculations show that, over its life, alternative 2 will save $313 over alternative 1.

Life Cycle Cost Analysis – HDTV

LIFE CYCLE COST ANALYSIS
Project/Location: Example
Subject: Large Screen High Definition TV
Project Cycle: 12 Years
Discount Rate: 6.0%

INITIAL COSTS	Quantity	UM	Unit Price	Alternative 1 42" DLP HDTV Est.	PW	Alternative 2 42" Plasma HDTV Est.	PW	Alternative 3 46" LCD HDTV Est.	PW
A. 42" DLP HDTV	1	EA	$1,700	1,700	1,700	0	0	0	0
B. 42" Plasma HDTV	1	EA	$2,300	0	0	2,300	2,300	0	0
C. 46" LCD HDTV	1	EA	$3,300	0	0	0	0	3,300	3,300
D.				0	0	0	0	0	0
E.				0	0	0	0	0	0
Total Initial Cost					1,700		2,300		3,300
Savings compared to Alternative 1							(600)		(1,600)

REPLACEMENT COST SALVAGE VALUE Description	Year	PW Factor	Alt 1 Est.	PW	Alt 2 Est.	PW	Alt 3 Est.	PW
A. Rep. 42" DLP HDTV	6	0.7050	1,700	1,198	0	0	0	0
B. Rep. 42" Plasma HDTV	8	0.6274	0	0	2,300	1,443	0	0
C. Resale Value	12	0.4970	0	0	(1,150)	(571)	0	0
D.	0	1.0000	0	0	0	0	0	0
Total Replacement/Salvage Costs				1,198		872		0

ANNUAL COSTS Description	Diff. Eacl.%	PWA	Alt 1 Est.	PW	Alt 2 Est.	PW	Alt 3 Est.	PW
A. Contract Maintenance	0.00%	8.384	120	1,005	90	755	140	1,174
B. Electrical Energy	0.00%	8.384	120	1,005	80	671	100	838
C.	0.00%	8.384	0	0	0	0	0	0
D.	0.00%	8.384	0	0	0	0	0	0
Total Annual Costs (Present Worth)		2.012		2,012		1,425		2,012
Total Life Cycle Costs (Present Worth)				4,910		4,597		5,312

Appendix L

Choosing By Advantages

Introduction

Choosing By Advantages (CBA) is a tested and effective decisionmaking system. It simplifies, clarifies, and unifies the art of decisionmaking. The development of the CBA system began centuries ago; however, much of the system was developed during the last half of the twentieth century. The art of decisionmaking is too large to be studied all at the same time. Therefore, CBA organizes the art of decisionmaking into three areas, so that one area can be studied at a time.

- **Sound decisionmaking** (making decisions that are anchored to the relevant facts) is the foundation of the CBA system. (This is where the CBA training process begins.)

- **Congruent decisionmaking** (making sound decisions that have unity, harmony, and integrity—and, accomplishing high-priority activities, projects, and programs on schedule) is the foundation and framework.

- **Effective decisionmaking** (making sound, congruent decisions that are willingly—or grudgingly—accepted and implemented) is the total CBA system.

Virtually all types of decisions, from the simplest to the most complex, call for CBA definitions, principles, and methods. The CBA system includes methods for very simple decisions, very complex decisions, and all types of decisions between very simple and very complex. The methods are unified by just one set of definitions and principles.

At least three of the definitions are presented early in the CBA training process:

- **Alternatives** are people, things, or plans from which one is to be chosen.

- An **attribute** is a characteristic, quality, or consequence of *one* alternative.

- An **advantage** is a difference between the attributes of *two* alternatives.

Two of the principles go hand in hand, as shown by the following questions:

Q: How can we humans consistently make sound decisions?

A: **The Anchoring Principle:** We must anchor our decisions to the relevant facts.

Q: How can we anchor our decisions to the relevant facts?

A: **The Fundamental Rule of Sound Decisionmaking:** We must base our decisions on the importance of advantages. (The system is called Choosing By Advantages to help people remember this rule.)

The Two-List Method, which is near the middle-level of complexity in the sound-decisionmaking area of the CBA system, has just three simple steps: list, decide, and choose:

1. **List the advantages (not attributes) of each alternative in the Two-List Format.**

2. **Decide the importance of each advantage.**

3. **Choose the alternative with the greatest total importance of advantages.**

CBA simplifies decisions that are simpler than those that call for the Two-List Method by taking fewer steps. For example, the Simplified Two-List Method requires just two simple steps. For most of our day-to-day and minute-to-minute decisions, even the Simplified Two-List Method is too slow. These decisions call for CBA methods that are much faster than the Simplified Two-List Method.

On the other hand, CBA simplifies more complex decisions by taking smaller steps. For some types of decisions, CBA divides the decisionmaking process into five phases (not to be confused with the phases of the Value Methodology Job Plan discussed in Chapter 6):

- **Phase I:** The Stage-Setting Phase
- **Phase II:** The Innovation Phase
- **Phase III:** The Decisionmaking Phase
- **Phase IV:** The Reconsideration Phase
- **Phase V:** The Implementation Phase

When a decision, or project, calls for a VM study, it is conducted in Phase IV. All the decisions that are made during a VM study call for CBA concepts and methods. (Obviously, none of the decisions that are made during a VM study call for unsound methods of decisionmaking.)

Learning CBA is much easier than learning mathematics. However, learning CBA is similar to learning mathematics:

- Both require the precise use of words and symbols.
- In each case, educators must teach just one set of concepts and methods at a time.
- Each new set builds on those that were taught before. Therefore, they must be taught in a particular sequence.

• People can immediately begin using (and benefiting from) each new set, as soon as they learn it.

In the evaluation phase of the Value Engineering Job Plan, some types of decisions call for the Tabular Method. An outline of the Tabular Method is shown below. The purpose of presenting it here is only to provide awareness of the method. To skillfully use this method, decision-makers need to learn the details. For example, they need to clearly understand the answers to the following and other sound-decisionmaking questions:

Q: Why would it be a mistake to base a decision on the advantages and disadvantages of the alternatives?

Q: Pros and cons are not the same as advantages and disadvantages. How are they different?

Q: Why would it be a mistake to base a decision on the pros and cons of the alternatives?

Q: Why is it impossible to assign correct numerical weights, ratings, or scores to factors, criteria, goals, roles, functions, categories, attributes, and so forth?

Q: What are the three principles and four considerations that must be applied when deciding the importance of each advantage?

Q: In the CBA process, what is the role of function analysis?

For the Tabular Method, two additional definitions are required:

• A FACTOR is an element, part, or component of a decision. It is also a container for criteria, attributes, advantages, and other types of data.

• A CRITERION is a decisionmaking rule or guideline. It is a standard on which a judgment is based. And, it is a decision that guides further decisionmaking.

Must-criteria rule out unacceptable alternatives during the innovation phase. In choosing a television, for example, the following must-criterion—"The television's screen size must be at least 42 inches"—rules out all televisions with a screen size less than 42 inches. **Want-criteria** come into play during the decisionmaking phase. They identify the least-preferred attributes in step 2a of the following outline.

An Outline of the Tabular Method

Try to memorize the words that are emphasized in this outline.

1. Summarize the **ATTRIBUTES** of each alternative, in the Tabular Format.

2. Decide the **ADVANTAGES** of each alternative.

   a. Underline the least-preferred attribute in each factor. (This makes it easy for someone reviewing the decision to clearly see its rationale.) If there are two that are the same, underline just one of them.

   b. In each factor, determine and display the differences from the least-preferred attributes. These differences are the advantages of the alternatives.

3. Decide the **IMPORTANCE** of each advantage.

   a. *Circle*, or otherwise highlight, the most important advantage in each factor. If there are two that are the same, circle just one.

   b. *Select* the paramount advantage—the most important of all the advantages (the most important of the most important). Assign an

---

importance score of 100 (or any other convenient number) to establish the top of the scale of importance for the decision.

c. *Weigh*, on the established scale, the importance of each remaining most important advantage, compared with the paramount advantage.

d. *Decide* the importance of each remaining advantage, again compared with the paramount advantage, and compared with each other. (Where there is no advantage, there is no importance.)

4. **Calculate the TOTAL IMPORTANCE of advantages for each alternative.**

If costs are equal, choose the one with the greatest total importance of advantages. If costs are not equal, initial and life cycle cost estimates should be developed at a level appropriate to the decision being made.

When costs are not equal, the decision requires consideration of the incremental importance/cost relationships among the alternatives.

Remember:

ATTRIBUTES

ADVANTAGES

IMPORTANCE

Circle, Select, Weigh, and Decide

TOTAL IMPORTANCE

Also remember that CBA simplifies more complex decisions than those that call for the previous outline by taking smaller steps. For a very complex decision, or project, the CBA process can take several months, or even several years. During the life of a major project, CBA definitions, principles, models, and methods are applied numerous times. For a very simple decision, the entire CBA process takes only a fraction of a second.

Example: Large Screen High Definition TV

Consider the example of the selection among three large screen high definition TVs. The attributes of the alternatives are shown in the following chart:

Factors	Alternative 1 42" DLP HDTV	Alternative 2 42" Plasma HDTV	Alternative 3 46" LCD HDTV
Screen size	42" screen	42" screen	46" screen
Sound quality	Very good	Excellent	Good
Image quality	Good	Very good	Excellent
Performance	Moderate	Low	High

The figure on page 179 is a tabular chart that illustrates the process outlined above. First, list the **alternatives** in the columns as shown. Next, list the **factors** in the rows.

Starting with the first factor, screen size, list the **attribute** in size for each alternative. Alternatives 1 and 2 have 42-inch screens, while Alternative 3 has a 46-inch screen. Underline one of **the least preferred attributes**, in this case, the 42-inch screen of Alternative 1.

Also in the first factor, determine the size differences from the least preferred attribute (the one that is underlined). These differences are the **advantages** of the alternatives. Alternative 2 has no advantage in this factor. Alternative 3 has 4 inches of additional screen size. This difference is the advantage of Alternative 3, in screen size. The **most important advantage** in this factor is the 4 inches of additional screen size and is circled.

Choosing By Advantages

Project/Location: Example
Component: Large Screen High Definition TV

Factors	Alternative 1 42" DLP HDTV		Alternative 2 42" Plasma HDTV		Alternative 3 46" LCD HDTV	
Screen Size						
Attributes:	42" screen		42" screen		46" screen	
Advantages:	-----	0	-----	0	4" larger screen size	50
Sound Quality						
Attributes:	Very good		Excellent		Good	
Advantages:	Better sound quality	30	Much better sound quality	40	-----	0
Image Quality						
Attributes:	Good		Very good		Excellent	
Advantages:	-----	0	Better picture	60	Much better picture	100
Performance						
Attributes:	Moderate		Low		High	
Advantages:	Better performance	40	-----	0	Much better performance	60
Total Importance of Advantages (Benefits)		70		100		210
Initial Cost	$1,700		$2,300		$3,300	
Life Cycle Cost	$4,910		$4,597		$5,312	

Continuing this process for the remaining factors (sound quality, image quality, and performance) identify the most important advantages, which are highlighted in the previous figure. Next, select the paramount advantage. Then, weigh the importance of each most important advantage.

For this example, the **paramount advantage** was "much better picture." To establish a scale of importance, it was assigned an importance of 100. The **other most important advantages** were then weighed, compared with the paramount advantage, using the same scale of importance. Much better performance received an importance of 60; the 4-inch larger screen size received 50; and the much better sound quality received 40.

Next, the decisionmakers decided the importance of **each remaining advantage**, on the established scale of importance. (Where there is no advantage there is no importance.)

Next, the **total importance** of advantages for each alternative was calculated. Alternative 1 has a total importance of 70, Alternative 2 has a total of 100, and Alternative 3 has a total of 210.

Since costs were not equal, the decision required consideration of the importance to cost relationships between alternatives. Using the initial and life cycle cost estimates prepared as part of LCC (see LCC discussion) resulted in the graphs shown as the figures on pages 182 and 183.

The Importance to Cost graph plots the cost on the X axis and the total importance on the Y axis. From the figure on page 182, it can be seen that Alternative 1 has the lowest initial cost and also the lowest total importance. Alternative 3 has the highest initial cost but also offers the greatest total importance. The figure on page 183 illustrates the comparison of importance to life cycle cost.

Alternative 1 is clearly not preferred since it costs more than Alternative 2 and has less total importance.

An opportunity-cost analysis revealed the following: Although Alternative 3 has the highest life cycle cost, it is still the preferred alternative. The incremental additional life cycle cost for Alternative 3 is justified by the large increase in total importance and is therefore recommended.

Importance to Initial Cost Graph

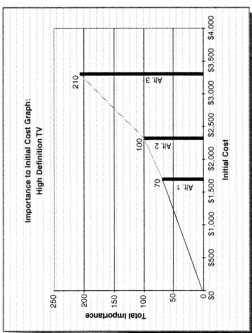

Importance to Initial Cost Graph:
High Definition TV

Total Importance

Initial Cost

Alt. 1
Alt. 2
Alt. 3

70
100
210

Importance to Life Cycle Cost Graph

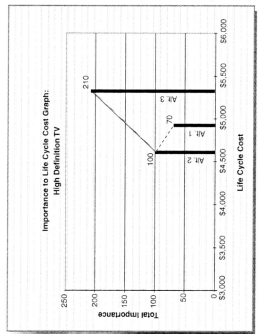

Appendix M

Value Improving Practices

Oil companies, chemical producers, pharmaceutical companies, forest product companies, and consumer products manufacturers enhance their capital productivity through the use of Value Improving Practices (VIPs). These VIPs are often used in evaluating a project's performance, deciding whether it should proceed to the next phase. The twelve VIPs are:

1. **Technology selection.**
2. **Classes of facility quality (project value objectives).**
3. **Minimizing standards and specifications/practices.**
4. **Process simplification.**
5. **Waste minimization.**
6. **Process reliability modeling.**
7. **Design to capacity.**
8. **Predictive maintenance.**
9. **Constructability.**
10. **Energy optimization.**
11. **VE.**
12. **3-D CAD design.**

VE is an integral part of the VIP process.

Appendix N

Introduction to the Value Dictionary

The Lawrence D. Miles Value Foundation was incorporated in 1977, and its first official project was to create a dictionary of value terms. The foundation created the College of Fellows, comprising the leaders in VM, to prepare these definitions.

The function of a dictionary, such as Webster's, is to:

- Define a word (single word).
- Establish a priority (of definition).
- Determine the range (of usage).
- Provide a spelling.

To avoid duplication and confusion with standard dictionaries, the standard definitions for VM include only two or more word groupings. Single word definitions have been left to traditional dictionaries. Terminology becomes unique to a technology through the use of modifiers (adjectives) to further define normally defined nouns. For example:

- Use value.
- Esteem value.
- Basic function.
- Secondary function.
- Job plan.
- Value Engineering.

- Value Analysis.
- Production cost.
- Overhead cost.

Refer to the foundation's web site (www.valuefoundation. org) for the complete Value Dictionary.

Value Dictionary

cost, acquisition—The price paid to procure a product not produced in-house.

cost, annualized—An economic technique to convert any defined set of present value costs to an equivalent, uniform, annual amount for a fixed period.

cost, application—See *cost, customer*.

cost, breakeven—(1) The point, for a given quantity of product, where the cost to purchase the product is the same as the cost to manufacture it in-house; (2) The quantity at which two competing acquisition alternatives are equal in cost.

cost, conversion—The money expended to convert raw material, or an unfinished product, into the desired, usable end product.

cost, customer—Product price of acquisition paid by a customer.

cost, development—(1) The amount spent on product research, design, models, pilot production, testing, and evaluation; (2) A cost normally considered product overhead and distributed as a fixed cost over an estimated number of products to be produced.

cost, differential—The difference in the life cycle cost between two competing alternatives.

cost, direct—(1) Cost that is directly identifiable with and attributable to the production of one specified product; (2) Cost that cannot be allocated to more than one product.

cost, direct labor—The amount expended for salaries and wages to provide a product.

cost, essential—All cost necessary to provide basic function.

cost, factory—See *cost, manufacturing*.

cost, fixed—(1) Cost incurred that is not dependent upon the quantity of products produced; (2) Cost that does not vary with the volume of business, such as property taxes, insurance, depreciation, security, and basic water and utility fees; (3) Expense for labor, material, equipment, and tools to produce the first product.

cost, function—(1) The proportion of product cost allocated to functions performed by the product; (2) All costs directly associated with the performance of a particular function; (3) Costs required for the realization of a function.

cost, general & administrative—A special classification of overhead cost normally apportioned to products and including salaries for executives, managers, and administrative and clerical staff, as well as general office supplies and equipment and marketing, and, as specified, including advanced design, research, and other administrative costs.

cost, incremental—(1) The difference in product cost between established incremental levels of product performance; (2) The add-on, alternative, accessory, or choice cost, which takes into account the availability of existing resources when adding a new system; (3) Also referred to as *cost, variance*.

cost, indirect—(1) See *cost, overhead*; (2) Also called indirect burden.

cost, indirect labor—The amount expended for employee benefits, such as retirement, health insurance, vacation, other time off, unemployment compensation, and bonuses.

cost, investment—The initial costs of product development, excluding sunk costs, which are assumed to occur as a lump sum in a base year.

cost, labor—The sum of direct labor cost and indirect labor cost.

cost, life cycle—(1) The sum of all acquisition, operation, maintenance, use, and disposal costs for a product over a specified period of time; (2) The sum of all costs for the development, procurement, production, and installation of a product, as well as for its financing, taxes, operation, logistic support, maintenance, modification, repair, replacement, and disposal over the period of its useful life; (3) In manufacturing, it is also referred to as the sum of development, production, and application costs; (4) The economic measure of value.

cost, logistic support—(1) The cost of spare and replacement parts and equipment with associated installation labor; (2) The cost of periodic maintenance and repair; (3) The cost for those activities necessary to plan for and provide support programs, such as logistics, field engineering, publications, supply support, spares, training, administration of logistic functions, and repair coordination; (4) In the military, the cost for details embracing the transport, quartering, and supply of troops.

cost, lowest total—The lowest life cycle cost.

cost, manufacturing—The sum of the costs expended for direct material, direct labor, and factory overhead costs for a product.

cost, material—(1) The cost expended for raw or purchased materials needed to produce a product; (2) Normally includes the cost for packaging, inspection, shipping, and delivery of purchased materials.

cost, non-recurring—(1) Items of cost that represent a one-time expense at predicted times in the future; (2) Normally includes the cost for packaging, inspection, shipping, and delivery of purchased materials.

cost, overhead—(1) Costs apportioned to products from overhead accounts; (2) Costs that cannot be specifically and directly charged to a single product as being solely incurred by that product, such as development, supervision, tooling, maintenance, heat, power, light, buildings, taxes, and financing; (3) Usually fixed costs; (4) Also called indirect costs or burden.

cost, ownership—(1) The cost to acquire, operate, maintain, repair, and dispose of the product during its period of use; (2) The cost to possess the product, including all finance charges, taxes, insurance, and loss of product use when it is out of service.

cost, product—(1) The sum of manufacturing, both general and administrative, and selling costs; (2) The total expense to produce a product; (3) The transfer of money, labor, time, or other personal items to achieve an objective; (4) One component of price.

cost, production—See *cost, manufacturing*.

cost, recurring—(1) Repetitive production costs that vary or occur with the quantity being produced; (2) Cost expressed in terms of a recurring, direct unit cost of production of an item consisting of labor, direct burden, materials, purchased parts, expendable tooling, quality control, test, inspection, packaging, and shipping; (3) Costs which are repetitive throughout a product's useable life.

cost, relative—(1) Differential costs between various products of functions, rather than actual or absolute costs; (2) Costs that show order of magnitude only and the order of expense from greatest to least.

cost, replacement—Future cost to replace a product or product component, which is expected to occur during the product's life.

cost, retrofit—The cost to incorporate a product improvement or necessary change into an older product.

cost, standard—(1) Cost calculated on accepted productivity and material rates, used as a norm against which to compare actual performance; (2) Costs accepted as the basis for budgeting or allocation of funds.

cost, supplier—The price a manufacturer pays for generally off-the-shelf purchased parts, materials, and supplies, as contrasted with subcontractor costs, which generally involve some degree of product manufacturing.

cost, total—(1) All cost for someone to acquire, use, enjoy, maintain, and dispose of a product, plus the time, effort, and risk of buying; (2) See *cost, life cycle*.

cost, unnecessary—(1) Costs for functions not desired; (2) Cost for quality or performance above that needed by the user; (3) Any cost which does not contribute to value; (4) That portion of the cost of a product that does not contribute to essential functions, required performance, or marketability.

cost, variable—Direct or indirect costs that change directly with the quantity of, or conditions under which, products are produced, as distinguished from fixed costs.

cost, variance—See *cost, incremental*.

cost, vendor —See *cost, supplier*.

---

function, aesthetic—(1) A function describing esteem value rather than use value; (2) A function attributable to pleasing the user rather than contributing performance; (3) A function that indicates product features that exceed its technical utility or performance requirement; (4) Also referred to as esteem value.

function, basic—(1) That which is essential to the performance of a user function; (2) The function describing the primary utilitarian characteristic of a product to fulfill a user requirement; (3) Also called primary or essential function.

function, critical—A combination of the basic and selected required secondary or dependent functions, defining the means used to achieve workability of the product.

function, critical path—One of the set of basic and dependent functions that meets the "how" and "why" logic on a FAST diagram, forming a path of essential functions without which the product would not perform.

function, dependent—(1) Lower order functions, to the right of each other on a FAST diagram, that are successively dependent on the one to its immediate left for its existence; (2) A function that depends on a higher order function for its existence; (3) A function that exists or is chosen in order to achieve a basic function.

function, essential—(1) A function describing a characteristic that is absolutely necessary to a product's ability to perform the user function; (2) Also called the necessary or required function.

function, esteem—See *function, aesthetic*.

function, higher order—(1) A function that is a goal rather than an objective or an objective rather than a task; (2) A function that is more abstract than specific, i.e., "feed people" is a higher order function than "distribute food stamps."

function, independent—(1) A function that does not depend on another function or on the method selected to perform that function; (2) A function that occurs all the time, i.e., a part or assembly may have to "resist corrosion," regardless of what other basic or secondary function that part is performing.

function, lower order—The opposite of a higher order function, that is, giving tasks rather than objectives, and being specific rather than abstract.

function, necessary—See *function, essential*.

function, non-essential—See *function, unnecessary*.

function, primary—See *function, basic* or *essential*.

function, required—See *function, essential*.

functions, required secondary—(1) A secondary function that is essential to support the performance of the basic function; (2) A function that may result from specified design criteria.

function, secondary—(1) The manner in which the basic function was implemented; (2) A function indicating quality, dependability, performance, convenience, attractiveness, and general satisfaction beyond that needed to satisfy minimum user needs; (3) Includes supporting unwanted, unnecessary, and required functions.

function, sell—(1) A function that provides primarily esteem values, such as "improve style" or "enhance decor"; (2) A function that may result from specified design criteria.

function, supporting—(1) A function required by the user to make a product sell; (2) A function that increases acceptance; (3) A function to assure dependability, assure convenience, satisfy the user, or attract the user; (4) Also called a sell function.

©2008 GOAL/QPC

function, task—See *function, user*.

function, unnecessary—(1) A function not contributing to the utility or desirability of the product; (2) Also referred to as a non-essential function.

function, unwanted—(1) A negative function caused by the method used to achieve the basic function, such as heat generated from lighting, which often must be cooled; (2) Also called an undesirable function.

function, use—See *function, work*.

function, user—(1) That function performed by a product that causes its purchase by a user; (2) The function performed by an employee for the company; (3) Also referred to as a task function.

function, work—(1) A function that is essential to make the product or service perform as intended; (2) A function that provides use value; (3) Also called use function.

value, present—The economic procedure to account for the time equivalent value of past, present, or future costs at the beginning of a base period.

worth, function—(1) The lowest overall cost that is required to perform a function; (2) The least cost attainable through the use of a functional equivalent; (3) The cost of a function without regard to the consequences of failure; (4) Referred to as the value of a function in some texts (not a preferred usage).

worth, present—See *value, present*.

year, base—The year to which all future and past costs are converted when the present value method is used.

Suggested Readings

ASTM Subcommittee E06.81 on Building Economics. *ASTM Standards on Building Economics*. West Consho-hocken, PA: ASTM, 2007.

Boothroyd, Geoffrey. *Assembly Automation and Product Design*, 2nd ed. Boca Raton, FL: Taylor and Francis Group, LLC, 2005.

Boothroyd, Geoffrey, Peter Dewhurst, and Winston Knight. *Product Design for Manufacture and Assembly Revised an Expanded*, 2nd ed. New York: Marcel Dekker, Inc., 2002.

Bralla, James G. *Design for Manufacturability Handbook*. New York: McGraw-Hill, 1999.

Dell'Isola, Alphonse J., and Stephen J. Kirk. *Life Cycle Costing for Facilities*. Kingston, MA: Reed Construction Data, 2003.

Duncan, Peggy. *The Time Management Memory Jogger*. Salem, NH: GOAL/QPC, 2008.

Helander, Martin and M. Nagamachi, eds. *Design for Manufacturability: A Systems Approach to Concurrent Engineering and Ergonomics*. London; Washington, DC: Taylor & Francis Group, Inc., 1992.

Kirk, Stephen and Kent Spreckelmeyer. *Enhancing Value in Design Decisions*. Grosse Pointe Park, MI: Kirk Associ-ates, 1998.

Suhr, Jim. *Choosing By Advantages Decisionmaking System*. Westport, CT: Quorum Books, 1999.

Wang, Ben. *Concurrent Design of Products, Manufacturing Processes and Systems*. Amsterdam: Overseas Publishers Association, 1998.

Index

39 Engineering Parameters, 143, 144

acquisition savings, 84–86

active verbs, 40

Akao, Yoji, 2, 116

Altshuller, Genrich, 2, 137–138, 140, 143, 146

Blast-Create-Refine Method, 58–59

Boothroyd, Geoffrey, 2, 136

brainstorming, 43, 51–52, 58, 60, 101, 121, 140, 146, 158

Bytheway, Charles W., 1, 95

categories and points, LEED, 160

certification levels, LEED, 160

Choosing By Advantages (CBA), 172–183
  example, 178–181
  importance to initial cost graph, 182
  importance to LCC graph, 183
  overview, 172–178
  tabular matrix of advantages, 179

combining functions, 43

combining ideas, 58

consensus, 30–31, 101–102, 104–105, 107–108

contractor's allowable development and implementation costs (CADIC), 84, 87

cost reduction, 4, 79

cost-ranking ideas, 57–58

customer voice, 114–119

Delphi, 101–108
  case study, 105–108
  design options, 102–105
  overview, 101–102

Design for Manufacture and Assembly (DFMA), 2, 127–136, 151
  advantages of, 133
  application of, 127–128
  organizational benefits, 130–131
  outsourcing and, 132
  overview, 127
  summary of methodology, 134–136
  teamwork and, 129–130

Design-Bid-Build Procurement Method, 13

Design-Build Procurement Method, 13

development phase, 61–66
  business case, 64–65
  technical case, 62–63

Dewhurst, Peter, 2, 136

Direct Magnitude Estimation (DME), 115–116

evaluation of data gathered, 38–39

Fallon, Carlos, 38

FAR 52.248-1 supply and services contracts, 79–87
  acquisition savings, 84–86

details of, 79–80

information contained, 80–81

negative instant contract savings (NICS), 84–86

reasons for rejection, 81–82

sharing rates, 83

FAR 52.248-2 A/E contracts, 87–90

FAR 52.248-3 construction contracts, 90–93

follow-up phase, 74–75

Forced Relationships Method, 56–58

Ford, Henry, 20

Function Analysis System Technique (FAST), 1, 18, 43, 95–100, 122–123, 125, 126, 191

conventions, 98–99

example diagram for major phase in product development process, 125

example diagram for manufacturing process, 123

functions, 95–98

overview, 95

procedures, 99

when to use, 99–100

functions

active verbs, 40

allocating resources to, 47

analysis and cost-worth, 45

basic and supporting, 39

calculating value indexes, 49–50

combining functions, 43

determining worth, 49

function worksheet, 44

measurable nouns, 40

multiple use functions, 43

operations vs. functions, 40

secondary, 46

simple words, 39–40

verb/noun lists, 40, 41–42

Galvin, Bob, 3

General Electric, 1, 3

General Motors, 2, 148

genka kaikaku, 109–110

Gordon Technique, 52

government contracts, 76, 77–79, 82, 90

group consensus, 30–31, 101–102, 104–105, 107–108

idea categorization, 56–57

ideas, combining, 58

ideas, cost-ranking, 57–58

implementation phase, 73–74

Isuzu, 2, 112, 148

Kaufman, J.Jerry, 148

Leadership in Energy and Environmental Design (LEED) checklist, 159–160

certification levels, 160

NC categories and points, 160

rating system, 160

Lean Enterprise Value (LEV), 120–126

life cycle costing (LCC), 10–12,
18, 62–64, 66, 67, 69, 71, 76,
88–89, 159–160, 161–171,
178–181, 188, 190

decisionmaker's influence
on, 10

discount rate, 165

economic principles, 162–163

overview, 161–162

present worth (PW) method,
163–165

time value of money, 163

management address, 38

management applications, 14

manufacturing, 13

McNamara, Robert, 3

measurable nouns, 40

Memory Jogger, 19, 23, 52, 120

Miles, Lawrence D., 1, 3, 25,
39, 51, 53, 61, 66

Mitsubishi, 116

morphological analysis, 52, 54

multiple use functions, 43

negative instant contract
savings (NICS), 84–86

Nested Hierarchy Process
(NHP), 116

net present value (NPV)
method, 163–165

OMB Circular A-94, 165

operations vs. functions, 40

outsourcing, DFMA and, 132

Pareto's Law of Distribution,
6, 9, 10–11

present worth (PW) method,
163–165

project overview, 38

prototypes, 9, 12

Quality Function Development
(QFD), 2, 116–117, 141, 150, 152

rating system, LEED, 160

Sato, Yoshihiko, 148

sharing rates, supply and
services contracts, 83

simple words, 39–40

Six Sigma, 3, 146

Society of American Value
Engineers (SAVE), 1, 50, 95, 148

Suhr, Jim, 172

supply and services contracts,
79–87

Table of Contradictions, 143, 145

target costing, 109–113

T-Charting, 59–61

team building, 23–24

team selection, 20–22

teamwork, 129–130

tear-down analysis, 148–152

steps, 149–152

types, 148–149

Theory of Inventive Problem
Solving (TRIZ), 2, 127, 137–147

background, 137–140

fundamentals of methodology,
140–146

---

overview, 137

as VM tool, 146

timing, 13

Toyota, 2, 109, 110, 112, 120

U.S. Green Building Council (USGBC), 159–160

Value Change Proposals (VCP), 8

value dictionary, 186–193

Value Engineering Change Proposal (VECP), 76–94

benefits, 77–78

FAR 52.248-2 A/E contracts, 87–90

FAR 52.248-3 construction contracts, 90–93

implementation, 78–79

overview, 76–77

rejection, 81–82

savings, 82–86

subcontractors, 87

supply and services, 79–81

Value Improving Practices (VIPs), 184

Value Policy Statement (VPS), 5–8

defined, 5

elements, 5–8

verb/noun lists, 40, 41–42

VM job plans, 25–37

application of, 25–27

facilitator preparation, 37

preworkshop activities, 27–36

VM job plans, postworkshop activities, 73–75

follow-up phase, 74–75

implementation phase, 73–74

VM job plans, workshop activities, 38–72

creative phase, 51–53

development phase, 61–66

evaluation phase, 53–61

function analysis phase, 39–50

information phase, 38–39

presentation phase, 66–72

VM performance indicators, 6–7

VM workshops, 15–19

choosing site, 15–16

facilitation skills, 18–19

required materials and logistics, 17

room environment, 16–17

weighted evaluation technique, 153–158

determining criteria and weights, 153–156

ranking ideas, 156–158

Welch, Jack, 3